C. W. Anderson's Favorite Horse Stories

C. W. Anderson's

collected and illustrated by
C. W. Anderson

E. P. Dutton & Co., Inc. New York

Favorite Horse Stories

Fourth Printing June 1969

ACKNOWLEDGMENTS

Permission to use the following material is gratefully acknowledged by C. W. Anderson and the Publishers:

HORSES ARE LIKE SOME PEOPLE From *This Was Racing* by Joe H. Palmer. Copyright 1953 by A. S. Barnes and Company, Inc. Reprinted by permission of the publishers.

STYMIE—COMMON FOLKS From *This Was Racing* by Joe H. Palmer. Copyright 1953 by A. S. Barnes and Company, Inc. Reprinted by permission of the publishers.

VELVET AND THE PIEBALD From *National Velvet* by Enid Bagnold. Copyright 1935 by Enid Bagnold Jones. Copyright renewed © 1963 by Enid Bagnold Jones. Reprinted by permission of Brandt & Brandt and William Heinemann, Ltd.

THE LAST CATCH From *Sun Up* by Will James. Copyright 1931 Charles Scribner's Sons. Renewal copyright © 1959 Auguste Dufault. Reprinted by permission of the publishers.

CHAPO—THE FAKER (including illustration on page 52) From *Will James' Book of Cowboy Stories*. Copyright 1951 Charles Scribner's Sons. Reprinted by permission of the publishers.

BILLY BARTON—A GALLANT ROGUE From *A Touch of Greatness* by C. W. Anderson. Copyright 1945 by The Macmillan Company. Reprinted by permission of the publishers.

THE BATTERED BRIGADE From *The Collected Sporting Verse of Will H. Ogilvie*. Published by Constable & Co., Ltd., 1932. Reprinted by permission of the literary executors of Will H. Ogilvie.

THE SPOTTED WONDER From *Donoghue Up!* by Steve Donoghue. Published by Collins Sons & Co., Ltd. and Charles Scribner's Sons.

BROWN JACK From *Donoghue Up!* by Steve Donoghue. Published by Collins Sons & Co., Ltd. and Charles Scribner's Sons.

OLE MAN SANFORD From *Hoofbeats* by John Taintor Foote. Copy-

A WORLD FAMOUS HORSE STORY LIBRARY Selection

Contents

Foreword 11

Horses Are Like Some People *Joe H. Palmer* 15

Stymie—Common Folks *Joe H. Palmer* 19

Velvet and the Piebald *Enid Bagnold* 24

John Peel *John Woodcock Graves* 35

The Last Catch *Will James* 37

Chapo—the Faker *Will James* 45

Billy Barton *C. W. Anderson* 56

The Battered Brigade *Will H. Ogilvie* 65

The Spotted Wonder *Steve Donoghue* 67

Brown Jack *Steve Donoghue* 75

Ole Man Sanford *John Taintor Foote* 81

The Look of Eagles *John Taintor Foote* 93

The Straight Goer *Will H. Ogilvie* 119

Putnam—U.S. Army 121

Pawnee *C. W. Anderson* 126

The Ride of His Life *David Gray* 133

Old English Hunting Song 141

Big Red *Arthur Bartlett* 143

Man o' War vs Upset *Willie Knapp* 160

Right Royal *John Masefield* 162

Cowboy *Ross Santee* 165

Colts in Pasture *Billy B. Cooper* 176

Eddie Arcaro and Whirlaway *Eddie Arcaro* 178

Eddie Arcaro and Citation *Eddie Arcaro* 184

Big Red *J. A. Estes* 190

Illustrations

Frontispiece
"This time he knew *he'd won."*   17
"He just gets so full of himself that he wants things to hap-
   pen."   21
"He was a natural jumper."   28
JOHN PEEL   35
"I wanted that black horse, I never stopped to think why,
   but I wanted him."   38
"He was standing still as a statue and looking up where his
   little bunch of mares and colts used to be at this time of
   the day."   42
"And when you might get to think you know and can trust
   him, he'll bust wide open with all the meanness that's
   really in him."   46
Will James, with pen and ink, the most difficult and inflexible
   of all mediums, could draw action that the fast action
   camera later verified in every detail.   52
"No horse was near him throughout the three-mile course
   and he won as he pleased."   59
"Billy soon won respect for the way he jumped the huge
   furze fences."   61
THE BATTERED BRIGADE   65
"He was big, strong, but his color was gray—a rare and
   unpopular color in those days—and he had weird white
   blotches on him that made him look something like an
   enormous edition of a child's rocking-horse."   68
"I find it hard to write of Brown Jack as though he were an
   ordinary horse, or even a horse at all. He was so much
   more."   76

"Of all the horses who have been a glory to our state, suh, but one otheh had as game a heart as this superb creature."   82

"But, suh, the hawss will race on his merits and without any sort of stimulant."   87

"The black colt."   112

"The look of eagles."   117

THE STRAIGHT GOER   119

"It was a quick, knowing eye with a glint in it. And the ears were very alert and always moving."   127

"He'd go around with his head in the air, his nostrils flaring, carrying his tail like a flag."   129

"Dooley bucking over from good ground, his rider with him, although well toward his ears."   135

OLD ENGLISH HUNTING SONG   141

Man o' War.   144

"The twenty-eight foot stride."   147

"He could do anything—and do it better than any horse that ever lived."   161

RIGHT ROYAL   163

"There's hardly a day I wasn't on some bucking horse."   167

Ross Santee first began to make small, rough sketches on his leather chaps with a burnt-out match. Later he worked with ink and brush from a Chinese laundry—the only art materials available to him in Arizona at that time.   169

"And every jump the sorrel took Mack raked him with his spurs."   173

COLTS IN PASTURE   176

"The one-eyed blinker."   180

"Riding Citation was like being on a machine equipped with a throttle. You opened it up and away he went."   185

"Everyone asserted that this was America's greatest race horse since Man o' War."   188

BIG RED   190

Foreword

Through the years, as my interest in horses grew, I collected all available material in this field. The collection of factual writing grew apace but the shelf devoted to fiction on the subject remained small. Having horses as constant companions gave me a realization of their qualities and characteristics and consequently made me more aware of what rang false in stories about them. Too many writers in this field have had little equipment for the task other than enthusiasm and a vivid imagination; not good substitutes for real knowledge.

From this shelf—a collection of thirty years—and from those stories of actual horses whose careers read like fiction, these are selected in the hope that the reader may have tastes akin to mine.

Many of these stories have long been out of print and so will be new to present-day readers. Will James and Ross Santee lived the life they wrote, and since they and the West they knew are gone, the stories are unique. Horses with such unusual personalities as Brown Jack and The Tetrarch, and riders with Steve Donoghue's perception and understanding may not come our way again.

And Man o' War! What anthology would be complete without him. As one noted turf writer said, "He was as near to living flame as horses ever get."

C. W. Anderson

C. W. Anderson's Favorite Horse Stories

Horses Are Like Some People

Joe H. Palmer

If Joe Palmer had been born in any state but Kentucky, he would undoubtedly have been a brilliant professor of literature at some university. He had all the qualifications. He was a Phi Beta Kappa, only a few months away from a doctorate, when the chance came to join the staff of The Blood Horse Magazine. *Devoting his whole time to studying and writing about horses was a dream come true to this Kentuckian. He wrote with a knowledge, gayety and humor not seen before in this field, and soon was asked to take over as turf editor of the* New York Herald Tribune.

He was liked by all associated with racing and breeding, and greatly respected for his knowledge which was always clothed in witty, ironic prose. His pen could cut as deeply as the sword of Cyrano when called for, and the pompous often felt its edge.

On one occasion a spokesman for the cheaper races—the claimers that helped fill the racing program—stated that these horses were really the "backbone of racing."

"The backbone?" wrote Palmer. "Well maybe. Pretty far down, though." (This and the following selection are from This Was Racing.*)*

The surest way to write a successful magazine piece is to write about men or women. For some reason which evades me, they do not seem to know much about one another, and prudery forbids an obvious suggestion. So articles about one or the other are avidly read.

Failing this, a man may always make the front pages with an article on the relative intelligence of animals. I mean other animals. In most of these the horse comes off badly, and it has come to be an article of faith with some of our sports writers that he is deficient in intelligence as compared to the other domesticated or semi-domesticated animals.

A horse cannot pile up boxes on a platform so he can get at a banana on the ceiling, because he has no hands with which to pick up a box and he doesn't like bananas anyway. He cannot very easily be taught to sit on his hindquarters and beg, because he cannot be easily supported in this position as a dog can be and because it's a damned undignified position for a horse or a political candidate, as horses realize and political candidates don't.

That doesn't mean the horse isn't smart, as will be freely granted by anyone who has watched the Lipizzans perform in Madison Square Garden, flowing through intricate maneuvers under what amounts to invisible guidance.

A favorite story in this corner concerns a horse you probably don't remember. His name was Sands of Pleasure, and he was the first good horse to come from the Fair Play–Rock Sand cross which was later made famous by Man o' War and others. Sands of Pleasure was a stakes horse in his early years, but as time went on he dropped down a little, and wound up running in claiming races. But like so many of the horses with the turbulent blood of Fair Play, he had his notions.

He was beaten a nose on the post one day. This was before the days of the finish camera, when the judges put up the numbers immediately and hoped they were right. The jockey on Sands of Pleasure came back, saw his number in the second slot and pulled up to unsaddle. The horse tried diligently to throw him, and afterward tried to wrestle down the groom who was holding him, and to kick several innocent bystanders.

The trainer was disturbed, because the Fair Plays were prone to grow moody and intractable as they grew older, which usually meant the end of their racing usefulness. So he tossed the horse into a race in which he didn't fit, a few days later, just to see, and Sands of Pleasure, beaten some five lengths, came back blowing a little, because he had given it a good try, but otherwise unruffled.

Well, if there's a secret to training horses, it's to understand how a horse thinks, and this trainer went to putting two and two together. Next time he started the horse, he gave the jockey some unusual instructions.

"I think you can win this if you get off fast," he said. "But if you do win it, don't come back to the winner's circle. Pull him out to the outside rail to unsaddle."

Sands of Pleasure took the track and held his horses, and won pulling up by several lengths. He came back to the grandstand and was guided to the outside rail, according to orders. The jockey afterward swore that the horse turned his head and looked at him. Then Sands of Pleasure took the bit firmly in his teeth and went into the winner's circle, where he belonged.

"This time he knew *he'd won."*

So the trainer had figured this one correctly. In that first race Sands of Pleasure had disagreed with the placing judges and thought he had won, and he took it badly that another horse was in the winner's spot. In the second he knew he had been beaten, and that was that. In the third he knew cursed well that he had won, and he was having no nonsense about it.

In those pre-camera days, it was the custom of all losing horse-players to insist that the judges were a set of purblind incompetents, selected for their duties after an eye test in which they not only couldn't pronounce the words, but couldn't see the letters. Sands of Pleasure thus proved himself to have about the same judgment as a losing horse player, which rated him close up behind the chimpanzee, and possibly ahead of the dog.

Stymie — Common Folks

Joe H. Palmer

On the cold blustery afternoon of January 28, 1921 several hundred persons huddled in the wind-swept stands of the old Kentucky Association track at Lexington to see one horse gallop past them. Down he came, a great red chestnut with a copper mane and a high head, flying the black and yellow silks of Samuel D. Riddle. This was Man o' War, leaving the racetracks forever.

Fourteen years passed before Lexington considered another horse worth a turnout. Then, on March 11, 1935, some 500 citizens assembled, on a foul, wet afternoon, to see Equipoise take his last public gallop. This was at the private track of the C. V. Whitney farm, because it was in that unbelievable, two-year period when Lexington had no public racetrack.

The next performance, and as far as I know the last one, came on August 8, 1943 when Calumet Farm celebrated "Whirlaway Day." By this time the Chamber of Commerce had got into the act, and there was a remarkable spate of Congressmen, Southern oratory, news cameras and radio announcers. This is not a complete list.

It is unlikely (though you never can tell about a chamber of commerce) that there will be any such doings over Stymie, when he arrives to enter the stud at Dr. Charles Hagyard's Green Ridge Farm. It isn't that the other three were Kentuckians coming home, and that Stymie's an outlander from Texas. It was thoroughly appropriate that Stymie should have his final public appearance at Jamaica, because he's a Jamaica kind of horse. Though I have no doubt he will do well in the stud, his kinship is with the racetrack, not the breeding farm.

Man o' War, Equipoise and Whirlaway all were equine royalty from the day they were foaled, Stymie was common folks. It is true

19

that he carries the blood of both Equipoise and Man o' War, but all pedigrees are purple if you go back a little. He was a son of a horse that had won two common races, out of a mare that couldn't win any. Nobody ever thought the other three were anything but good. Stymie began as a $1,500 plater that couldn't get out of his own way.

Stymie wasn't, of course, as good as any of the three. But he was immeasurably tougher. Could he have got to the races one more time he would have started as many times as all three of the others together. If you want to clutter your mind with a perfectly useless bit of information, Man o' War made his reputation by blazing nineteen miles and five furlongs; Equipoise, stopping now and then to grow a new hoof, ran just a trifle over fifty miles in competition. Whirlaway lasted a little longer, and lacked half a furlong of running sixty-six miles. But Stymie's journey to leadership among the world's money winners took him 142 miles, plus half a furlong and sixty yards. That's more than the other three together.

Man o' War and Equipoise and Whirlaway each won the first time out, at short odds, as they were expected to do. Stymie was 31 to 1 in a $2,500 claiming race and he ran as he was expected to do, too, finishing seventh. He was out fourteen times before he could win, and that was a $3,300 claimer.

You are not to imagine that Stymie was accidentally and mistakenly dropped into a claiming race before anyone appreciated his quality. He ran twelve times in claiming races and got beat in eleven of them. He was, until the fall of his two-year-old season, right where he belonged. Then, from this beginning, he went on to win $918,485.

This is, you will see, basically the story of the ugly duckling, of Cinderella among the ashes, of Dick Whittington and his cat, and of all the world's stories none has ever been preferred to that which leads to the public and very glorious triumph of the oppressed and downtrodden. Jamaica's horseplayers are to some extent oppressed and downtrodden, and perhaps in Stymie they find a vicarious success.

The horse envisioned by a breeder in Kentucky or elsewhere, is the son of a Derby winner out of an Oaks mare, which can sweep the futurities at two and the classics at three, and then come back to the stud to send other great racers to the wars. These are, roughly, the specifications which fit such horses as Citation and Count Fleet and War Admiral, and the like.

But the racetrackers, I think, save most of their affection for the Exterminators and the Stymies and the Seabiscuits, who do it the hard way in the handicaps, pounding out mile after bitter mile, giving weight and taking their tracks wet or dry, running for any jockey, and trying with what they've got, even when they haven't got enough. That's why Stymie fitted a farewell at Jamaica better than a welcome in Kentucky.

"He just gets so full of himself that he wants things to happen."

He's a curious horse, this obscurely bred Texas product. This tourist leaned on Jack Skinner's back fence at Middleburg one December for maybe a half hour, just studying Stymie, which did not return the compliment, but went on picking at the scanty winter grass. Except for the crooked blaze which gives him a devil-may-care expression, he's the most average horse you ever saw. Not tall, not short, not long, not close-coupled. Good bone, good muscle, good chest—nothing outstanding, nothing poor. As a result, of course, he is almost perfectly balanced, and maybe this is what makes him tick.

However there is another matter. When Stymie comes to the peak of condition, he exudes vitality so you expect to hear it crackle. He comes to a hard, lean fitness that you seldom see in domestic animals, unless in a hunting dog that has been working steadily, or perhaps in a hunter that has been having his ten miles a day over the fields. This is when, as Hirsch Jacobs says, he gets "rough." It isn't temper or meanness. He just gets so full of himself that he wants things to happen.

The faster he goes the higher he carries his head, which is all wrong according to the book, but is a characteristic of the tribe of Man o' War, to which he is inbred. This tourist, who doesn't scare easily in print, will long remember the way Stymie came around the turn in the Pimlico Cup Handicap with his copper mane flying in the wind, making pretty good horses look as if they had just remembered a pressing engagement with the quarter pole.

He is not a great horse in the sense that Man o' War and Equipoise were great. He isn't versatile. There are many dozens of horses around that can beat him at a mile, and even at a mile and a quarter he would have trouble with Armed or Lucky Draw, just as he had trouble with Devil Diver. He can't make his own pace and he can't win slow races. He needs something up ahead to draw the speed from the field, to soften it up for his long, sweeping rush at the end.

But give him a field with speed in it, at a mile and a half or more, and horses had better get out of his way, even Whirlaway.

Anyway, another fine and ardent and satisfactory story of the turf was brought to a close at Jamaica. And it was happy to note that, for all the long campaign, it was no battered and limping warrior that left us. Stymie never looked better with his bronze coat in great bloom, and the high head carried as proudly as ever.

As he stood for the last time before the stands, people around the winner's inclosure were shouting to his groom, "Bring him in here, for just one more time."

The groom didn't obey, and probably he was right. Stymie never got in the winner's circle without working for it. It was no time to begin.

Velvet and the Piebald

Enid Bagnold

National Velvet is, I feel, one of the most delightful horse stories of all time. The novel is not to be confused with the movie of the same name. Little but the title was retained in the Hollywood version.

The plot is pure fairy tale, but the development of character and incident have such authenticity that the impossible becomes completely convincing. First of all there is Velvet, with adoration in her eyes, walking through the hot grasses to touch, for the first time, that marvel, The Pie, that she was to win in a raffle; her silent mother, a huge woman, who in her youth had swum the Channel breaststroke; and young David, whose imagination was such that it alone had reality. And there is Mi, her father's helper in the butcher shop, who was only a little less than God to Velvet and the other youngsters. Here then is a selection from a book that will always remain a classic. (–From National Velvet)

In the end Velvet took Sir Pericles and rode alone to Tablet Gully.

In Tablet Gully the piebald cropped, moving from tuft to tuft in sun and shadow, and flashing as he moved. The bone of his shoulder, thrown up by his stooping neck, rippled under his sliding skin. His parti-colored mane hung forward over his neck, and his long tail tipped the ground.

He swung round with the sun. His teeth tore evenly as he worked. Now his quarters could be seen, slightly pear-shaped and faulty, but strong. His hocks, too thick, but straight and clean, waded in the burnt grasses. He lifted a sloping pastern finished with a pink hoof, and bit a fly off his leg. The clouds reared overhead,

24

the legendary gully with its dead man's tablet was heavy with steady sun and shielded from the wind.

Among the scabious flowers on the north slope sat Velvet, steady as a gorse-bush, cross-legged, and watching the horse. She had tied Sir Pericles to a gate in the valley behind her.

Sitting like a Buddha, dreaming of the horse, riding the horse in dreams. A piece of cake and a Mar's Bar beside her in a paper bag, and the insects hummed and the mauve August flowers hardly moved. Just to look at him her heart beat violently with ambition. Her strong and inexperienced imagination saw no barriers. She was capable of apprehending death and of conceiving fame—in her own way, not for herself but for her horse. For a shilling she had won this wild creature that did not know its strength. In this valley, tucked away, she had got glory. What she meant to do made her heart beat afresh. She looked steadily at the piebald as though she pitied him. Eating his grass, prince, with his kingdom waiting for him! Her hand stole out and pulled the Mar's Bar from its bag, and she sucked its heavy stump, made from milk chocolate, toffee and nuts.

All the Hullocks were creeping with dowdy animals at livery. But here in Tablet Gully moved on its clever legs this living horse. Pulling gently at a blister on her heel she rode him in her mind. She would dazzle the world with this spot of luck, she and the creature together, breathing like one body, trying even to death, till their hearts burst. She would place her horse where he belonged, in history. She clasped the Mar's Bar like a prophet's child, with both hands.

"Leaders have been cut from coaches to do it . . ." she whispered as she rose. "Even horses out of carts. Why not him?"

A halter made of rope lay behind her and picking it up she walked gently down the valley holding it behind her frock. The piebald stared at her, interested. He loved humanity, and had it not been for the exceptional grass in Tablet Gully would have been off to the village long before this.

Frankly he watched her come, nostrils slightly distended and both calm eyes upon her, the blue eye and that white eye where the pied color streaked across his cheek. She paused beside him and slipped the halter over his head. He shook his neck to free it from flies and came with her willingly.

They reached Sir Pericles, who snorted at sight of them and danced his hind-quarters, looking from side to side, catching his soft nose on the reins. How could his mistress walk so out of valleys leading horses? He was intrigued and excited, jealous, pleased to see her again. Velvet loosed and mounted him, and the piebald walked sedately at their sides, striking out his fore feet in his own peculiar gait.

They reached a field not far away, enclosed by a stone wall, and Velvet changed the saddle and bridle, tying Sir Pericles with the halter to the gate. She mounted the piebald, and walked and trotted him quietly in large circles. His mouth was a mixture of lead and rubber. He had no notion how to obey the bit but imagined that to turn his neck was all that was wanted. He would trot onwards with his neck turned to one side like a horse that has no face. Velvet had to rock him with her knees to get him out of his orbit, and even then it was no more than a bewildered stagger to one side. She set him into a canter. It was clumsy and gallant, and accomplished with snorts. He flung his powerful white head up into the air and nearly smashed his rider's precious plate. Sir Pericles watched. The flashing piebald snorted excitedly round the field. Above him sat the noble child, thin as famine, bony as a Roman, aquiline nose and domed white forehead, tufted loonily with her cotton hair. Velvet, with her great teeth and her parted lips, her eye sockets and the pale eyes in them, looked like a child model for a head of Death, an eager, bold, young Death. She was thinking of something far outside the field. She was thinking of horses, great horses, as she sat her horse.

Turning in a flash in the middle of the field she drove him on with her knees. They went at the wall together. Over the grasses, over the tufts and mounds, both knitted in excitement, the horse sprang to the surge of her heart as her eyes gazed between his ears at the blue top of the flint wall. She bent slightly and held him firm and steady, her hands buried in the flying mane firm on the stout muscles of his neck. She urged him no more, there was no need, but sat him still. He was a natural jumper. She did not attempt to dictate to him. They cleared the wall together, wildly, ludicrously high, with savage effort and glory, and twice the power and the force that was needed. Velvet felt his hindquarters drop when they should have hitched. But there was so much space to spare that the piebald could afford it. Nevertheless it was an intemperate and outlandish jump.

She rode him back to his own valley and loosed him, then returned home alone on Sir Pericles, parading in dreams. As she approached the village she was outlined against the sunset, on the brow of a Hullock. Stirrups short, angled knee and leg etched on the side of the saddle; childish, skeleton hands waving with the ebb and flow of the horse's mouth on the reins; hands that seemed knotted and tied like a bunch of flowers with streamers going from them, swinging together, knuckle to knuckle, thumb to thumb, while she sat erect above them, her face held on the wand of her body. The straw hair floated and stared above the wide-open eyes.

Sir Pericles walked like Velvet sat. His soft mouth held the snaffle as a retriever carries a bird. Yet he arched his neck as though his bit were a bit of thorns, and his long, almond, Chinese eyes looked both backward and forward at once. He seemed to be watching from either end of the agate stuff that was his window, watching Velvet's leg, watching the horizon before him. The oxygen in the evening air intoxicated him. In the eye of little Sir Pericles something soft and immortal shone.

Velvet had laid down the piebald and her ambitions and was thinking comfortably of the coming gymkhana. In her mind she rose at white-painted gates and fences. Her knees crisped with her thoughts in the saddle and she leant forward. Sir Pericles never altered his tossing walk. His head and tail, both like plumes, flirted, and he walked within her dream with a spot of gold upon his eyeball.

It was not the silver cup standing above the windblown table-cloth that Velvet saw—but the perfection of accomplishment, the

"He was a natural jumper."

silken co-operation between two actors, the horse and the human, the sense of the lifting of the horse-soul into the sphere of human obedience, human effort, and the offering to it of the taste of human applause. All this she had learnt already from the trained mouth and the kneeling will of Sir Pericles.

And as the dim sense of this understanding sighed up and down her body it entered too into Sir Pericles' nerves, and through his nerves to his comprehension. Velvet lived her round of jumps, lips parted, the sunset shining on her golden mouth. She rose and fell at the triple bar, the water-jump, the gate, the imitation wall. She heard the hands, palm on palm, threshing the noise of applause. Sir Pericles dreamt it too, a wild dream beyond his understanding, but to be recognized when the taste came again.

His hoofs came down sweetly on violets, grass and knitted thyme, clanking on a flint, breaking the crisp edge of a wheel rut. He took in everything, behind, before, and from the body astride him. Below, the chimneys were smoking up like poplars and a light was lit in the cobbler's shop.

They sidled together down the steep grassy banks towards the village.

"Velvet!" said Mally out of the darkness by the bottom gate.

"That you, Mally. Open the gate."

"Who's wired it up like this?" Mally wrenched at the twist of wire. She opened it and horse and child passed through. "The piebald's out again. Nobody knew you bin riding him but us. Came thunderin' down the street ten minutes ago."

"Where's he now? Father angry?"

"Went down to the sea as usual, an' slid about. Went crackin' up a side street. Father doesn't know. Better not let him. He's bin carrying on about the horses. It would be the limit if he found the piebald had started cracking down the street again."

"F'e broke a leg!" said Velvet in a voice of horror. "F'e did! Might. Easily."

"You can't go after him now. It's pitch. Thurs stars coming."

Sir Pericles gave a whinny. There came a sharp, near answer, and the piebald stalked out of the shadows, gleaming in the dusk.

"He's here!" Velvet's marvelling whisper, as she slipped off Sir Pericles and held out her hand. The piebald came nearer, breathing hard.

"Mount, mount!" said Mally. "Get on again! He'll follow. He won't think you want to catch him."

"What'll we do with him?" said Velvet as she scrambled back.

"I'll go an' get a halter and we'll try an' put him. . . . Put him in Miss Ada's box to-night and put her in the toolhouse!"

The piebald followed, threshing his head, snorting the pleasant village smells, till they reached the yard of the cottage. He drooped his neck for the halter like a horse born in a kitchen. Soon Miss Ada stood among the spades and shovels.

"Poor old darling Ada," said Velvet, as she pushed the shovels to safety behind a wooden case. "Get half the bedding from the loose-box, Mally. The piebald won't miss it. He's never had any before. I'll get Ada some oats to make her happy."

"What'll father say . . . about the piebald being in?"

"He won't know. I'll take him back early in the morning."

"Bet he neighs in the night. We'll shut both doors. He might try and jump the bottom one. Let's give him . . . What'll we give him?"

"Just hay," said Velvet. "He's not accustomed to oats."

"D'you know . . ." said Mally suddenly, pausing with an arm-ful of hay.

"What?"

"He'll be worse than ever after this. He'll be coming back every night to get a night's lodging and a supper! You never saw . . ."

"What?"

"The way he came down the village street, slipping and sliding and snorting and his eyes shining."

"He's like a prince!" said Velvet.

"Eh?"

"Just a thing I thought," said Velvet. "I pretend he's a prince."

At supper everyone ate with memories behind them. Edwina had been kissed by Teddy for the first time. Her nails had shocked and enchanted him. Merry had oiled the canary's stump, and was worrying about what she should call him. She had got a list of gods' names and a birthday list of girls'. It was so hard to know the sex of canaries.

Mally and Velvet were thinking of what they had got in the stable, the prince who might kick up a row in the night. Donald was asleep now, stitches in his foot, blood and spit mingled in his dreams. He yelped from time to time in his sleep like a puppy.

"Whur's Jacob?" said Mr. Brown suddenly as he ate.

"After they bitches," said Mi, with resentment.

"Seem bad this August."

"Bitches? Terrible they are. Crown's got one an' Ede's got one. That Jacob he . . ." Words failed, and slightly redder than before Mi continued to eat.

As the door opened for the pudding's entry they heard the impatient hammer of a hoof on wood. Mr. Brown continued to munch his bread. Mi sat up and his eyes flickered upon Velvet's face.

"I'm not hungry any more. Can I get down, mother?" said Velvet.

"Say your grace," said Mr. Brown.

"F'whatayave receivedthankGod," said Velvet, pushing her chair in, and went out in the dark. At the corner of the yard and the road four apple trees were enclosed by a broken fence. They were laden with little sweet apples and the ground was littered with the wind-blowings. She gathered two handfuls and went to the stable with them.

Mi hung about the yard all the evening, whistling for Jacob and looking down the road. Once he opened the top portion of the loose-box and looked in, grinning.

"Gettin' on all right?" he enquired. Velvet was sitting on the manger.

"He's quiet while I'm here," said Velvet. "But I can't stay here all night. Where's father?"

"Gone down to finish the bills," said Mi. "I thought he better."

Later in the evening Mally swinging on the gate by the apple trees saw Jacob coming up the empty road.

"Bitches good?" she asked him, flinging him a block of lichen off the gate post.

"Succulent," said Jacob, making a half circle round her.

"Go an' tell Mi about it!" said Mally.

Jacob went, bowing and grinning. Mi walloped him and gave him his supper.

Later in the night the house was quiet, the piebald quiet (for he had Velvet in her nightgown sitting on his manger), the moon rose steadily. At two o'clock the moon began to sink. Mi came to the stable door and looked over the top. He wore his sleeping clothes, several old sleeveless jerseys, and a pair of shorts.

"Get to bed now," he said. "I'll do a bit."

Velvet lowered off the manger. "Here's six quarters left," she said, pointing in the manger. "Give him a piece every time he seems restless."

"What is it?"

"Apples," said Velvet. "I bin feeding him bits all night."

"You'll make him loose," said Mi. "Where's the sacking pieces?"

"In the corner. An' ties. Ties off the hay bales."

At five the sea was running up with a gale behind it and pounding in the sewer. The day broke in flashes of light and the elms soughed in the wind. The piebald's tail and mane were flung about as Mi led him out into the yard, his hooves bound up in sacking. Velvet met them in the road.

"How'd you wake?" asked Mi.

"An't bin asleep," said Velvet. "I just heard the wind. Isn't he good!"

"Perisher," said Mi.

"Oh, no," said Velvet. "Oh, no. Wait while I get a bridle."

She returned with a snaffle-bridle belonging to Sir Pericles, one which they had brought in to clean the night before.

"Gimme a leg up, Mi," and he jumped her on to the warm, round back.

"Key of the field's behind the manger. Come up an' help me get Sir Pericles. I got to ride back on him."

Mi walked beside her up the road to the field in the gale.

"Blowing awful up there," he said, looking to the Hullocks.

"Seaweed's smelling like drains," said Velvet, looking at the wild and shining east.

" 'Tis drains," said Mi, sniffing. "Lota nonsense they talk about seaweed. You had anything to eat?"

"No, I forgot."

Mi grunted with disfavor. "Fer a sickly girl you give yerself something to do!" he said.

"An't sickly. M'wiry," said Velvet. "Shove the gate wider. I'll stub my knee!"

Sir Pericles trotted down gladly, tail flying.

"Halter's under the stone in the corner," said Velvet.

Mi picked it up. Sir Pericles came willingly enough. The two horses hustled clumsily through the gate.

"Good-bye," said Velvet and went off across the reedy ditch, riding the piebald and leading the chestnut.

"Why don't you ride the other?" shouted Mi, but his voice blew back into his mouth as he called into the gale coming off the sea.

He watched the horses go up the chalk road and break into a canter on the crest. His old mackintosh flapped on his bare legs and the wind tore at the roots of his red hair. "If she were a boy . . ." he said longingly to himself. With that light body and grand heart he would get her into a racing stable. He knew of many up North. He had friends here and there. She'd be a great jockey some day. Fancy wasting those hands and that spirit and that lightweight on a girl. "No more'n a skeleton," he said. "An' never will be, likely. She'd ride like a piece of lightning. No more weight'n a piece of lightning." He thought of her mother . . . . and of his old father. "Velvet an' her. A feather an' a mountain. But both the same."

Boom . . . went the sea on the cliffs. The savage blow came up the valley. Mi hated water. Brought up by the Channel trainer he had edged back inland as soon as he could. He couldn't stand the waves and the empty trough that sucked and soaked along the lip of the beaches. It turned his head, and he went up the village whenever he thought of the sea. "How she ever!" he thought, with his mind's eye fixed sharp on Mrs. Brown. Great, wallowing woman, half submerged, water pouring backwards and forwards over her shoulders, threshing across the water like a whale. A stormy dawn when she had landed. "Bet old Dan was pleased," he thought. "Wasn't many swimming the Channel those days."

His mind went back to Velvet. He too, like her, was longing to place his dream in history. This child, Velvet, was good for something.

He turned back to his bed, shivering, Velvet in his thoughts.

And hungry, sick, delicate, blown so that she could hardly breathe, Velvet in the grip of horses and of the gale went on across the blunt and unprotected Hullocks. Great skies slipped out of the folds, unfurled, and stood a thousand miles above her. The sight battered against unseeing eyeballs, was drunk into the marrow of something older than her brain. Flags and pennons and beacons waved above the high land as she sat below, thinking in slow brown drops of thought, sure of her future, counting her plans, warm in expectation, glorious butcher's Velvet, eyes cast down upon the moving shoulders of mortal horses.

John Peel

John Woodcock Graves

D'ye ken John Peel with his coat so gay?
D'ye ken John Peel at the break of the day?
D'ye ken John Peel when he's far, far away,
With his hounds and his horn in the morning?
    For the sound of his horn brought me from my bed,
    And the cry of his hounds which he oft-times led,
    Peel's view-halloo would awaken the dead,
    Or the fox from his lair in the morning.

D'ye ken that bitch whose tongue in death?
D'ye ken her sons of peerless faith?
D'ye ken that a fox with his last breath
Cursed them all as he died in the morning?

Yes, I ken John Peel and Ruby too,
Ranter and Ringwood and Bellman and True;
From a find to a check, from a check to a view,
From a view to a death in the morning.

And I've followed John Peel both often and far
O'er the rasper-fence and the gate and the bar,
From Low Denton Holme up to Scratchmere Scar,
When we vied for the brush in the morning.

Then here's to John Peel with my heart and my soul,
Let's drink to his health, let's finish the bowl:
We'll follow John Peel through fair and through foul,
If we want a good hunt in the morning.

D'ye ken John Peel with his coat so gay?
He lived at Troutbeck once on a day;
Now he has gone far, far away;
We shall ne'er hear his voice in the morning.
    For the sound of his horn brought me from my bed,
    And the cry of his hounds which he oft-times led,
    Peel's view-halloo would awaken the dead,
    Or the fox from his lair in the morning.

The Last Catch

Will James

Will James was born in a covered wagon in Montana in the days when the West was really the West. Buffalo, Indians, and longhorns were commonplace. He got his first horse—a small, black pony, at four, and was seldom afoot after that.

He had no schooling and was self taught in reading, writing, and drawing. His only textbooks were saddle catalogs and old magazines found around ranch camps. Drawing was his great enthusiasm, second only to riding.

In his day the high speed camera was not developed, so all the marvelous action we see in his drawings was what he himself saw and memorized. The action of a galloping horse is more easily observed and analyzed than the violent and varied actions of a bucking broncho, yet for a couple of centuries no artist had a sure enough eye to see that action accurately.

That James, with pen and ink, the most difficult and inflexible of all mediums, could draw action that the fast action camera later verified in every detail seems all but unbelievable. When it came to action he was near the top in a rare group; the natural-born draughtsman.

He wrote as he talked—a colorful, untutored language that often said much more than the precise English of other writers. Since he wrote only of what he knew from his own experience, his stories have an authenticity often lacking in fiction. The world he lived in and the men who made it are now gone but should not be forgotten.
(—From Sun Up. *The selection following is from* Will James' Book of Cowboy Stories.)

I'd been at Sand Wash camp for near a week before I noticed that up on one of the high ridges and hiding amongst the junipers, sunning themselves, was a bunch of wild ponies. They was backed up against a high rocky ledge which not only sheltered 'em from the cold spring winds but reflected the heat of the sun on 'em.

Then again it was a fine place for 'em to doze and sun themselves on account that the only thing that could very well get up there was mountain goats; they was safe enough from mustang runners, and if any ever did ride toward 'em they could always see 'em first.

I'd noticed how they'd be at that spot near every morning when the sun shined, and also noticed their tracks where they come to water at night, a mile or so above my camp.—An old corral was up there and showed, the way it was built, that it was a mustang trap at one time. Many had been caught in it I could see, and when the mustangs was thick, but now it was down in spots and I noticed it'd been neglected for quite a spell.

The water came out of a spring right inside of that corral and sunk in the ground a few feet away, still inside, and that's where that little wild bunch was watering.

My mustang-running fever raised up again when I thought how

"I wanted that black horse, I never stopped to think why, but I wanted him."

easy I could trap that bunch by just fixing up that corral and close the gate on 'em as they came in. I'd run and caught many a wild horse and still remembered the thrill, but now I was punching cows for a big outfit once again, had a steady job, lots of good broncs, good camp and good grub—and I tried to forget mustangs and how easy it'd be for me to catch that little wild bunch that was up on that ridge, but they was always up there reminding; I felt the wild-horse fever getting me and I was trying hard to keep it down.

And most likely I could of kept it down too, only, one day I happened to get a closer view of the black stallion that was in that bunch and the mustang fever had a hold of me once more—I wanted that black horse, I never stopped to think *why*, but I wanted him.

The days was long, and after my day's ride was over I'd go to the corral and try to fix it up so it'd hold the black horse and his bunch. I was mighty careful in the fixing too, on account that a too big a change in the corral would be noticed by the mustangs and if they got suspicious they'd go and water somewhere else.

But with a few live junipers and pinons with the branches and all still on, I managed to make everything look natural, and strong enough to hold any wild horse.—In a few days I was ready, fresh tracks showed that the mustangs came in to water as usual every night, and one night I took my stand by the trap and waited.

It was along about the middle of the night when I heard the wild bunch coming up the sandy wash, the sound they made brought back many memories and my heart was thumping again. Right on up they came and acted like they would walk right into the corral without any hesitating. That would be too easy, I thought—but there they stopped and bunched. I could tell by the snorts they was suspecting that all wasn't well, but as nothing stirred and all seemed as usual, they finally lined in.

I could make out the outline of the black horse as he stood with head up while his bunch was drinking, that long heavy mane, curved neck, and pointed ears was easy identified. All was inside and I was about ready to pull the rope that'd close the gate when, for no reason that I could see, the band stampeded and scattered

out like a bunch of quail a-snorting and shying. I could near touch
some of 'em, so close they passed by.

I figgered right there that my chances for catching the black
horse that night was gone, but he hadn't drank yet and maybe he'd
come back. He was out there with his bunch and I could hear him
nicker, the same as to ask if everything was all right as he scouted
around 'em.—Then when all got quiet once again and I kept a-
waiting, I finally heard a horse coming; pretty soon I could make
out a black shape, the stallion was coming in to have his drink,
alone.

That's just what I wanted—the black stallion alone, for I didn't
care for any of the rest—and when he put his head down to drink I
pulled on the rope and closed the big pole-gate with a bang.

I couldn't sleep very well the rest of that night on account of
wanting to see that black at close view and with the sun a-shining
on him, the first light of day found me awake and waiting for it. A
hunk of pitch pine soon had the little stove a-roaring, the coffee pot
begin to sing and by the time I'd went and caught me a saddlehorse
and came back, the coffee was boiling; a cup of that and a cigarette
and I was riding up the wash toward the trap corral and the black
horse.

I'd no more than got sight of the top poles of that corral when a
long whistle and a snort told me he was still there, and as I rode up
I found a quivering picture of horseflesh that was sure good to look
at, and that's all I did for a while was look; the more I looked
though, the less I liked the idea of putting a rope around that black
shining neck, for sometimes a rope sure does take the hair off in
spots.

But I was too excited just then to worry about what a rope could
do to a horse that fought it, and as I kept a-watching and admiring
every move that black was making, and noticing the deep heart, the
short back, and the long sloping hip that was some of his good
points, I was natural-like uncoiling my rope, and making a loop.

He fought like a wild-cat when that loop settled over his head
and drawed up back of his ears, but I was riding my best ropehorse

that day and, with the brand new rope I'd saved for such a purpose tied hard and fast to the saddle-horn, I knowed I had him for keeps. Being careful of keeping the slack out of the rope, so as none of us would get tangled up in it too much, I edged my horse toward the corral gate and opened it.—I was going to take him to another corral close to my camp.

The distance to that corral, with the black horse pulling on the rope for all he was worth, was sure covered plenty quick, but when he got sight of the new corral, he started another direction from there and I had to do considerable manœuvring to get him through the gate and into it. Next was to put the hackamore on him and tie him up.

I'd planned to start breaking him right away, but I wanted to take my time at it and do a good job, and as luck would have it, cattle begin scattering and straying away right about then, my time was all took up with 'em and I'd hardly ever get back to camp till away after sundown. As it was, the only chance I had to see my black horse was early in the morning and before I started out for a day's ride.

Things went on like that for quite a few days, and then I begin to notice something wrong, the black horse was ganting up pretty bad, wouldn't eat and wouldn't drink and I was getting worried. I'd give him plenty of fresh hay and even turned him loose in the corral, thinking it'd help, but all that attention didn't seem to better things any with him; the only thing that seemed the same was his spirit, he'd show plenty of that every time I walked in the corral, but there again I could see what kept that up. I'd often caught him looking up toward that big rocky ledge where him and his little bunch used to sun themselves—and that finally got to working on me.

I'd think of that often as I rode along through the day and somehow the more I thought on the subject the less satisfaction I was getting out of the idea that I'd caught the horse and had him in my corral, all safe for whenever I wanted him. And then soon enough I realized—, it wasn't owning the wild horse that made me want to go after him so much, it was the catching of him that

"He was standing still as a statue and looking up where his little bunch of mares and colts used to be at this time of the day."

caused a feller to get the mustang fever, and after the mustang was caught and the fever cooled down—well, I'd kinda wished they'd got away.

I'd quit running the wild horse on that account, and here I was with another one I'd just trapped and took the freedom away from. I had more horses than I could use as it was and what would I do with this one, sell him? not hardly. I was too much married to them ponies I already owned and I knowed it'd be the same with the black horse, I'd never sell him even though I had no use for any more.

I'd been running them thoughts through my mind for quite a few days and had come to no conclusion, and every morning found me making tracks toward the corral where I'd smoke a cigarette and watch my black horse—the hay I'd give him would hardly be touched.

Then one morning I started the fire as usual, put on the coffee pot and walked out toward the corral. I figgered on coming back before the fire died down, but as I set by the corral I forgot everything but the little horse there with me and the country around us. All was quiet excepting for a meadow-lark tuning up on a juniper close by. I felt like just setting there breathing in and listening—and I was thinking, thinking as I watched the black horse. He was standing still as a statue and looking up where his little bunch of mares and colts used to be at this time of the day. Finally I stood up, took in every line of him, like for the last time, and then I leaned against the corral gate and opened it slow and steady and *wide*.

The black horse seen the opening, and maybe it's a good thing he took advantage of it right then, for a minute afterward I felt like kicking myself for letting such a horse go; but that feeling didn't last long and instead, it done me good to watch him pace away, head and tail up, and seemed, like hating to touch the ground for fear another trap would spring up and circle him once more. Then, as I watched him disappear out of sight, I felt relieved—Somehow, he was better to look at that way.

The coffee had boiled over, put out the fire, and scattered

grounds all over the stove when I got back to camp, but I felt sorta cheerful and whistled a tune as I rebuilt the fire and put on fresh coffee.

A few days later I tore down the mustang corral by the spring and snaked the posts away with my saddle-horse. Then one morning I seen the black stallion and his bunch again; they was up by the big rocky ledge and just a-sunning themselves.

Chapo — the Faker

Will James

Few saddle horses are the size Chapo was. The name Chapo didn't at all fit him and maybe that was why he was called such. For Chapo is Spanish for a small, chunky horse and this Chapo was everything but that. He wasn't only tall but broad and weighed close to thirteen hundred pounds, the weight of a good size draft horse. But he carried that weight mighty well, was proportioned and built about perfect, and he had a quick fast action of a nine-hundred-pound cowhorse.

Mighty few saddle horses of his size are much good for fast and hard range work. Such horses are used mostly for corral work, snubbing or heavy roping, or "riding bog" (pulling out bogged down cattle). But when such a size horse is a good one, meaning in action and what all the smaller horse is, he's usually a *very* good one, as good as he's rare.

Chapo was one of that rare kind. With all his size he was active as a cat. He was very much that way when I come to work for the outfit he belonged to and was turned in my string. But he was of no more use by then, even tho he was still of good age, fat as a seal and had never been hurt.

He'd turned tricky, and fact was, as the foreman frankly told me, he hadn't been rode for a couple of years on that account. That was all the foreman told me about the horse, which is considerable more than a cowboy is usually told about any horse when he hires out to any outfit. If he's told, especially by the other riders, he won't listen, for he's apt to be told just the opposite of how this or that horse might act. That's done partly in a joking way but more to test the newcomer as to his experience—if he's a top hand, medium or of no account, if he's rode far and wide, is a home guard or just green.

"And when you might get to think you know and can trust him, he'll bust wide open with all the meanness that's really in him."

That's usually guessed pretty close soon as the new hand catches the first horse in his string. A string ranges from six to sometimes as many as fourteen head of different kinds of horses for different uses, to each rider, and the cowboy who's rode far and wide, for big outfits and is a good hand doesn't ask about any horse in the string that's turned over to him, nor listens to what he might be told about 'em. With his experience in handling more than many and all kinds of horses, he practically can tell the caliber of most any horse by a glance of him and the second his loop tightens around that horse's neck. If not then, he'll usually find out at the first sitting.

But some horses, not going the humans one better, don't show their true caliber until some particular thing happens. That might not show up until after a dozen rides, and when you might get to think you know and can trust him, he'll bust wide open with all the meanness that's really in him, catch you napping and get you, all depends on your sense of riding and general knowing of horses.

It would of been as well for me, or maybe better, if that foreman had not told me about Chapo being tricky. I didn't ask him in which way, but just the look, actions and great size of that horse was enough to warn any cowboy who dabbed his rope on him.

He stopped sudden, turned and faced me quick as my loop settled over his head, and holding it high he followed my lead, snorting, out of the bunch. Well, I figured right there, he sure wasn't a jerk-away anyhow, and that was one fine point, especially when a rider is off his horse and many miles away from camp.

With his head held high the way he did, he looked as tall as a giraffe and my five feet eleven more like that of a pigmy. But for a horse that hadn't been rode for a couple of years, and fat and good feeling as he was, I didn't think he was so bad, just acting natural. It was also natural when he struck at me a couple of times as I come up the rope to within touching distance of his nose. I was expecting that, and to put an end to such action I flipped the end of my rope around his front feet. I seen then too, the way he just stood and trembled, that that had been done to him plenty times before and well busted (thrown) when he run against it.

Watching his hind hoofs, which might reach up quicker than I could see, I then put my twisted rawhide hobbles on his front ones. The next was to slip my hackamore on his sky-high head, and there's where I had the beginning of some trouble, for he was mighty head-shy and would hardly let me touch it. But by going easy I managed to work a half hitch over his nose and I could then touch him up to his eyes. I got the hackamore that far, and there I was stuck, for he held his head not only near out of my reach but jerked it as I'd try to get the hackamore headstall over his eye and close to his ears, and as he'd jerk that way he'd rear and strike with both hobbled front feet. But I'd be close to his shoulder at such times and the flying hoofs would graze past.

I seen then, as I tried to ease the hackamore headstall over his eyes on up, that he had a "bug in his ear." Sometimes such head and ear shyness *is* caused by a bug, maybe a wood tick that gets in the ear and makes a sore. But with Chapo I could see it was only plain fear of being eared down, which I found out afterwards had often been done so'd he wouldn't kick the rider while getting on or off of him.

After his two years of freedom he was of course much touchier about that left ear of his, and no matter how easy and careful I tried, I couldn't get my hackamore above his eye. But I'd had dealings with such horses before, so, instead of trying to slip the hackamore from the front and over his eyes up to his ears, I unfastened the headstall, slipped it around his neck to the back of his ears, where I wanted it, and fastened it there. He didn't seem to mind that so much, and being that on a horse broke to the bit I also used a bridle over the hackamore, I slipped it on his head in the same way.

Bridling was about the worst about him while handling him from the ground, and by easy stages I gradually broke him of that, for I didn't twist his ear to get on or off him, even tho at different times I come near having to do it.

He wasn't so bad to saddle, not if he was hobbled and you didn't jab him in any way the while. When such happened he could bring up a hind hoof and kick well ahead of his shoulder point, from a standstill and even tho hobbled. As I've already said he was active and limber as a cat.

I figured I was sure due for a tough ride the first time I prepared to get on him. It's always best to expect the worst and be ready, but what I was leery of the most was them far-reaching hind hoofs of his as I'd go to get on, that would be one of his tricks.

Without taking the hobbles off and standing well by and ahead of his shoulders, I took a hold of the "bosal" (hackamore nose band) and bridle cheek with my left hand. Chapo stood a-quiver at that, like ready and expecting me to reach for the stirrup. I felt that, and so, instead of reaching for the stirrup with my right hand, I reached for the saddle horn, wiggled the saddle some to make sure it was on tight enough to stay, and then, to the tense horse's surprise, I of a sudden doubled up with both knees to land high on his shoulder, to ride alongside there and just ahead of the saddle.

Well . . . That horse like to've had a cat fit at that trick, which I seen right away had never been tried on him before. I was too high for him to reach with a hoof, and as he went up in a wide-winding buck-jump, being hobbled and out of kilter, he near doubled up on his neck instead of landing on his feet as he came down, and I, being free, easy cleared his fall.

I was again on his shoulder before he got entirely to his feet but he didn't do much high flying jumps any more after that, just circled sideways some and tried to whirl me off. . . . When he finally come to a standstill and while all a-puzzled, I slid down to the ground, took off the hobbles and then eased into the saddle without him hardly seeming to realize. Anyhow he didn't make a move.

And when I did move him, and sort of made him come to with a light pop of my quirt, it was my turn to be surprised, for instead of lighting into the powerful and hard bucking as his actions all indicated he was sure aching to do, he just went to crowhopping, then to bucking, but not hard enough to throw even a stool-riding drugstore cowboy off.

I must of looked my surprise, for a few of the riders that was near had to laugh, and I was then told that that was about the worst bucking he ever done.

I rode Chapo when his turn come, every two or three days, and thought he was a good circle horse (for roundup rides). The tricks I'd so far found in him wasn't any worse than could be expected from most circle horses, for them are horses that can't very well be used as cowhorses. They're usually the kind that take no interest in the ways of handling stock, and it's up to the cowboy riding 'em to put 'em to work in covering the country, rounding up and driving whatever stock is found to gather all in one herd at the "cutting grounds" (where what stock is wanted is held and the not wanted cut out; that's cowhorse work).

The circle horse string is usually made up of mature colts, cold-jawed and spoilt horses. Tough ones, and it don't matter so much if they can't be turned on a dime, as the good cowhorse can do, so long as they can stand a good ride at good speed, and can be turned to within a hundred yards more or less while chasing and rounding up stock.

After riding Chapo for about a month, whenever his turn come, I got to figure that the worst of his tricks was when I handled him from the ground. I finally cured him of them pretty well, but according to what the foreman had told me of him I kept a-thinking there sure must of been more and worse tricks than the ones I'd found to make the foreman pass that remark and warning. I had other and worse horses in my string than Chapo was and nothing was said of them. So I kept a-thinking there must be some other and still worse tricks in him which hadn't as yet come to the top or he sure wouldn't been left to run loose for two whole years. Not on account of what few tricks I had discovered in him.

I wouldn't of course ask the foreman as to what trick or tricks he meant Chapo had, for, as range etiquette points out, it's not the proper thing to do. So, as I'd be riding him once in a while I'd be wondering, and sort of curious as to what hidden tricks Chapo might have deep in him, which he'd be apt to bust out with most any time. That made me keep alert and sort of tense and ready for when one would pop, and that's where I felt it would of been better if the foreman hadn't warned me of Chapo's trickiness. I figured I could of been a match to any of 'em.

But as it was, always on the watch out as I rode him, he sometimes got me to do some scary wondering. Like for instance, when riding him on the top or steep side of a high peak that horse seemed to sense that I was anything but bold and brave when up so high in such places. Maybe he felt it by the way I hugged my saddle so tight and was so much nicer to him away up there.

There come one especial time, while I was riding him amongst steep pinnacles, high razor-back ridges and narrow ledges, when that horse kept a-spooking and gave me about all the scares I could stand for a spell. This was in a badland strip of country, deep ravines and near bottomless holes. But there was some pretty fair feed took hold in crags and amongst the little brush in some places. The wilder cattle would hit for such country during roundup time and hide away in there. Consequences was, that rough country had to be rode much closer than the more open.

I think I rode my saddle closer when I did the country that time, for Chapo seemed to enjoy scaring the life out of me by acting up at the most dangerous places, like spooking at his own tail, even saddle strings, and other things he wouldn't spook at any other time. He'd then hump up, jump around some and like he would go into a bucking or stampeding fit, right in such places where even a mountain goat would be careful of every step and the missing of one would mean a downward trip to China.

I somehow managed to live thru the scares, combed my scope of what cattle there was in it, and them being plenty fat and wild they didn't need chasing when once found out. They just left that country at the sight of me and as tho it was haunted, and the echo of my holler, when I wasn't too scared to, worked as if spooks was on their tails.

My circle done and finally getting out of the badlands to catch up with what cattle I'd scared out and thrown with more bunches other riders had got out, the scares that Chapo horse had given me begin

Will James, with pen and ink, the most difficult and inflexible of all mediums, could draw action that the fast action camera later verified in every detail.

to sort of react on me, against him, for now that the most dangerous places was past he was as well behaving and willing as he'd
been spooky, ornery and stubborn before.

That made me peeved to the point where, as I thought on his
scary tricks, I finally got good and mad at him and decided to take
all the orneriness out of him right there and then, also whatever
other streaks of trickiness he might have away deep in him. I was
seeing red, but I gave him his head so he'd be free to bring on all
the action he wanted and all to his heart's content as I hooked him
in the shoulder and unlimbered my quirt on him.

The first jump he made liked to broke my back. But I'd asked for
that battle, and at it we went. I'm sure that, according to what the
boys had told me, that Chapo bucked very much harder then than
he ever had before. He done a sure enough powerful job of it and I
wished some of the boys had been near to see for I knew they'd
agree with me. I was high and wide from my saddle quite a few
times during the battle, and I wasn't mad no more now as I kept
dragging my quirt on him all I could, I was just determined,
determined to whip all that orneriness out of him and whatever
more he'd been storing, and to win that battle, I had to.

And I did, even if it was nip and tuck a few times. . . . When he
finally throwed his head up and broke into a crow-hopping run I
was glad of it, for I'd had about enough too.

It was a couple of days later when it again come his turn to be
rode, seldom over half a day to the turn, for we changed to fresh
horses three times a day. He was snorty as ever before when I
caught him, like he'd forgot all about the battle we'd had and of his
losing it.

I knew his caliber and that what ornery streak was in him could
never be taken out. He'd have that in him for as long as he lived
and was able to navigate. But what still stumped me was what trick
or tricks was it that the foreman remarked of that horse having. It
sure must be odd and special ones, and which hadn't showed up yet.
I'd sure given him all the chances and encouragement to bring out
all the bad that was in him, and even tho he'd turned on most every
trick and twist a horse could the last time I'd rode him, there'd been

nothing much out of the ordinary from what all a good tough and ornery horse would do. So, by that and the foreman's remark I figured there must be still more to come.

Thru curiosity I come near asking him, but again thinking the better of it I decided to forget about it and take that horse as he come. Him and me had only that one battle and after that we got along well, as well as could be expected.

Then, a short time afterwards, when it was again his turn to be rode I noticed as I caught him that there was a sort of halfway meek look in his usually watchful and challenging eye. He was also some easier to bridle and saddle. I got on him without feeling I had to watch for a hind hoof, and when I started him out for that morning's ride he went along like a good one.

Even the other riders noticed that difference in him, and there was grinning remarks such as, "Maybe he ain't feeling well," or "I guess it's a change of heart," and so on passed around.

The last remark, the one about a change of heart kind of stuck to me. Maybe, I thought, the ornery son of a wolf did decide to change to the good, maybe a long pondered on conclusion from the good battle we had. Then, I thought again, or was it that he'd pondered on the other trick or tricks of his which the foreman had remarked about. . . . Maybe he was scheming on that now, to catch me napping.

But he wouldn't catch me napping, I figured, or getting too careless. . . . Nothing happened, only, when just a few miles from camp, I thought I felt him favoring his left front leg. A ways further on I was sure of a limp in that leg, and then, a couple of miles more and that horse was sure enough lame. . . . Too lame to go on and it would be plenty hard enough to get him back to camp, I thought, so as to unsaddle and turn him loose.

That lameness all come on him before we got to a point where the foreman would scatter us riders to different points, to circle and comb the country of what stock was there, driving all to the roundup grounds, near camp.

As we rode along, I noticed the foreman looking at my limping horse and sort of grinning to himself. I wondered about that, also that he didn't seem at all concerned about the horse's lameness. But I was, and was about to tell him I'd be turning back when he beat me to it, and grinning some, he just said, "All right, Bill. We'll see you in camp at noon."

It then came to me as I turned Chapo back for camp that there was something queer about his kind of sudden lameness, without a run, twist or jump to cause it. Then the foreman's knowing grin. . . .

It came to me all the plainer as, a ways after I'd turned the horse towards camp, he begin to lose his lameness, until before I got there it was practically gone. I knew then what was up. That wise Chapo had faked that lameness, and when he was again turned loose with the remuda (saddle bunch) there wasn't a sign of a limp in him.

I'd had horses fake in different ways with me before, but none had acted the part quite as well as Chapo had, and another thing, whether Chapo had been faking or not there's sure no pleasure in riding a lame horse. There was many others, and mighty, mighty few ever fake.

That noon, during the change of horses and as I caught another horse, the foreman told me that now Chapo would play lame for some time, maybe until roundup was over, then hide out on some other range when time for the next roundup come.

He was a wise one. If he couldn't outdo his rider, and one got the better of him after all his tricks had played out, he'd always fall back on the one trick such as the one he'd played on me and finally won. That was his hole card and the trick I'd wondered about. Fake lameness.

Billy Barton

C. W. Anderson

This is not fiction. Billy Barton was one of the great steeplechasers of his day. He hated the race track and showed his dislike so violently that he was ruled off—just as a tough boy is expelled from school. But racing over the jumps—a much more difficult and dangerous game—was right down his alley. Maybe he wanted things that way—as tough as possible. (–From A Touch of Greatness)

The development of a horse is usually along consistent lines—the game horse develops still more resoluteness, the quitter is always stopping a little farther from the finish, the rogue continuously becomes more cunning and impossible. Therefore, to depart from the beaten path, this story deals with a horse that was ruled off the tracks as a "rogue" and who became one of the greatest and gamest steeplechasers that ever raced through the field. His name was Billy Barton.

The term "rogue" has a wide range in its application. On the race track it means a horse that resents all discipline, that will not "break" with his field, and refuses to extend himself in a race. Of course he may be merely a smart horse who does not like racing and has decided to have none of it. At any rate, it is pretty safe to guess that he is an individualist.

There have been horses whose performances in this field would make Billy Barton seem a model of deportment by comparison. For example, there was the English horse Santoi, who could have been a champion except that he was so contrary he would do everything by opposites. When the field broke from the barrier he went Billy

56

Barton one better. Instead of standing stock still he went back-wards. The harder he was urged the slower he went. When you tried to turn him to the left he went to the right. Only when the brilliant American jockey, Tod Sloan, outsmarted him by accident did he run his race.

Sloan had a reputation for handling difficult horses. In the parlance of the turf "they ran for him." So it was a challenge to his skill to try to win with the rogue Santoi. However, the horse proved too much even for this skillful horseman and the field was half a furlong away before Santoi finally decided to run. When Sloan saw his fine turn of speed he thought he might at least make a showing by closing a lot of ground, so he started urging the horse on. Immediately Santoi began pulling himself up. In complete disgust Sloan tugged at the reins to bring him to a halt and instantly the contrary animal began going his best pace. The harder his rider pulled the faster he went.

Impossible as it may seem, the records show that Santoi won the Select Stakes and Sloan was questioned by the stewards because it looked from the stands as if he were trying to "pull" the horse.

Billy Barton was not as contrary a horse as Santoi, although he was always a strong-willed fellow. Even in his old age he decided who could come into his box stall and who could not. And if he did not want you it was best for your health to stay out.

In his early career he was a good performer and won his share of races but he was always what is called "a bad post horse." Whether this was due to the rough handling unruly starters got from the ground crew at the old fashioned barrier is not clear. But he became a rebel and finally refused to break at all. No amount of "schooling" did any good and the stewards barred him from further racing.

Many a fine campaigner begins to turn sour or cunning after many seasons of racing, refusing to extend himself, evidently figur-ing that he has done enough. Occasionally one like Display or Billy Barton decides to do things his own way early in life. We may call them "rogues" and "stupid brutes" but it is well to remember that it takes a courageous horse to stand up against man, who has all the odds in his favor. It is the rebel, not the conformer, who needs the courage.

Billy Barton was of royal breeding. His sire, Huon, was by Ard Patrick, winner of the English Derby, who in turn traced back in male line to the immortal St. Simon. His dam was a granddaughter of the fine horse Hermit, so his breeding was of the best. St. Simon was a horse with plenty of temper and many of his sons inherited it, as well as his great speed, so that the tough, willful brown horse may have come honestly by his rebellious disposition.

Shortly after Billy was ruled off the track, Howard Bruce, Master of the Elkridge Hunt, and a fine and understanding horseman, bought him, thinking to make a hunter of him. He was gelded and put to hunting and he took to jumping as a duck to water, making a name for himself in that part of the country where brilliant hunters are plentiful. Obviously, Billy and his new owner saw eye to eye, for his manners also improved so tremendously that he was trained for timber racing the following season.

Under the handling of that skillful gentleman rider of the day, Albert Ober, Billy Barton began a racing career over the jumps that is without parallel in that field. His first start was in the Grand National Point to Point at Brooklandwood.

Stuart Rose, noted gentleman rider, saw the horse for the first time on that occasion and wrote his impressions in his book on the Maryland Cup: "I recall that as they went to the post several riders galloped out a bit to warm up their mounts. It was at this time that I first noticed Billy, the brown gelding. Even in this perfunctory canter he displayed the most amazing ground-eating stride I had ever seen . . . I have never before or since seen a horse I liked better."

As this comes from a man who has ridden many and seen most of our great jumpers, it gives an impressive picture of the former rogue. In the face of Billy's past reputation, he was lightly considered by the hunting crowd present, which had seen many a fast flat runner come to grief over this type of jumps.

Consequently, neither the other riders nor the majority of the

"No horse was near him throughout the three-mile course and he won as he pleased."

spectators took the brown horse too seriously even when he was over the first fence—a solid plank affair four feet high—a length in front, nor even when he increased his lead to three lengths at the second. As one jump followed another, with Billy increasing his lead and fencing like a veteran, several riders tried to move up to him without success, for the brown horse had race-horse speed. No horse was near him throughout the three-mile course and he won as he pleased.

In his next start Billy performed the sort of feat that happens only in dreams or in movie plots—and very fancy dreams and melodramatic movies at that. Many of the riders who got nothing but a view of Billy's quarters in the Point to Point had let it be known that they wouldn't permit the brown gelding to steal away to such a lead as he did in that race. Hence, it was certain there would be a lot of pace in the race, the Maryland Cup, for many horses were entered that had a high turn of speed. Nevertheless, Billy was leading over the first fence and by the time they reached the big third fence he was three lengths in front.

On around the rolling green course one horse after another tried to challenge the brown gelding's lead, but none could maintain that pace for long and one by one they fell back. Billy's rider, meanwhile, was sitting still, letting Billy make his own pace. Then Burgoright, a fast and brilliant chaser, came with a rush to run head and head with the pacemaker. After clearing the eighteenth fence, Billy opened up a notch and moved to a length lead.

The pace was now very fast, especially so for such a course as this. The Maryland Cup fences are nothing to be trifled with, for the rails are big and strong and they rarely break. Billy, going at a terrific pace, misjudged the nineteenth fence, hit the top rail and went down. Burgoright sailed over and went into the lead, seeming to have the race won. But he was a horse at his best only when he had opposition. Coming into the twentieth fence with nothing near him, he swerved and refused. Put at it again he bungled the jump, hit the fence, and dropped his rider on the other side.

At this point Ferngrass, an outsider, came up. The field had many casualties that day—in fact only three of the twenty-two starters finished without a fall. As Ferngrass came into the twentieth fence, with only two more fences to the finish line, she looked the certain winner. But apparently from nowhere another horse appeared beside her, and rose to the fence with her.

As the newcomer outran Ferngrass to the next fence he was recognized as Billy Barton. Billy had been remounted, and had made up a world of ground to be again in the lead. He steadily increased his lead while going to the last fence and as he galloped over the finish line an easy winner, it was seen that the reins were all on one side of his neck. When the horse fell, the rider held onto the reins and was up instantly, vaulting into the saddle, but with Billy flying along he had no chance to adjust the reins.

That Billy Barton, the former rogue, took those last fences clean and true, entirely on his own, without a horse beside him, and with his rider little more than a passenger at that point, speaks volumes

"Billy soon won respect for the way he jumped the huge furze fences."

for that gallant jumper. To cap a story already top-heavy with improbabilities, Billy broke the course record by more than twenty-three seconds!

A brilliant campaign followed. Billy Barton was all but unbeatable in the big jumping events and he became the hero of the hunting and steeplechase followers. He won, among other races, the Meadowbrook Cup, the Pennsylvania Hunt Cup, the New Jersey Hunt Cup, and the Virginia Gold Cup. In the New Jersey Hunt Cup he was left at the post and not only overcame this handicap to win, but cut seventeen seconds from the course record. He was to hunt racing what Greyhound was to trotting and Man o' War to flat racing; a performer so outstanding that it is hard to say if we ever really got to the bottom of him.

By this time there was nothing left for him to do on this side of the world and it was decided to send him after that blue ribbon event of all steeplechases, the Grand National at Aintree, England. He hardly looked like a "National" horse to the English, who were accustomed to the big, raking seventeen handers that usually made up the Aintree fields. He was hardly larger than Battleship, known as "American Pony," before he showed the way around that tough course.

Billy soon won respect for the way he jumped the huge furze fences and his speed on the flat was also noted. But the long ocean voyage and change of climate and conditions retarded him in his training so that he did not fully reach the peak of condition needed for that grueling course of four and a half miles with thirty big fences. Had not Americans backed him so enthusiastically in the future books, Mr. Bruce would have withdrawn him.

When the field lined up for the start it seemed clear that there was to be plenty of trouble on the course, for it was the largest field in the history of the race. The break came raggedly and Easter Hero, one of the favorites, was off in front with Billy Barton alert enough to be off well with the leaders. When they came to the dreaded drop of Bechers, with many horses already down, Easter Hero was still setting the pace and Billy was going well in sixth place. By the time the Canal Turn was reached Easter Hero was five lengths in front but here disaster awaited him.

He jumped too soon, landed on top of the thick solid furze fence, and hung suspended, thrashing wildly about. In an instant the scene was a wild melee, with horses swerving and coming down in a tangle. Billy was hemmed in and had no chance to avoid the debacle. He had to take the jump as it came.

Putting in a tremendous leap, he cleared both the fence, which was huge enough in its own right, and the struggling horse perched atop it, leaving behind an evergrowing scene of disaster. No other horse would even attempt this terrifying obstacle.

At the eleventh fence only six of the original forty-two were still in the race and as the stands were reached the Americans were cheering wildly, for their hero was in the lead.

Becher's loomed big and menacing the second time around and took a further toll of tiring horses. Now only three were left—Great Span, Tipperary Tim and Billy Barton.

A fence or two more and Great Span's saddle slipped and threw the rider, causing the horse to swerve into Billy. Visibly tired, the American horse evaded the interference enough to keep his feet and the three horses headed for the last fence, Billy on the inside, the riderless Great Span in the middle and Tipperary Tim on the outside.

It was an anxious moment, for if Great Span refused he would knock one of the other horses out of the race.

They rose together, but Billy came into it low, dove through it and pecked on landing. For a moment it looked as if he might recover but his tremendous efforts had taken their toll. He fell heavily and Tipperary Tim was left to stride on alone.

Billy Barton, remounted, was the only other horse to finish. Had he stayed up over that last jump there is little doubt that he would have won, for few steeplechasers could match his speed on the flat. The tremendous effort he made to avoid disaster at the Canal Turn, particularly when he was not yet at his peak of condition, would have been enough to have caused his fall at the last fence. At any rate, Billy Barton received a singular tribute, for in all the books on the Grand National, whether published here or abroad, he is the one non-winner who receives as much space and notice as the winners.

He tried for the race a second year and was well placed and going splendidly when a falling horse directly in his path brought him down and cost him his chance. It apparently was not in the cards that the great little gelding was to win this event.

Without that victory his record still is exceptional. He was good and he was game—and at worst you might say he had the strength of both his prejudices and his convictions. Horsemen that know him always speak of him affectionately as Billy. Speaking of his disposition, they say "that rascal," not "that rogue."

The Battered Brigade

Will H. Ogilvie

The mark of a stake in the shoulder,
   The brand of a wall on the knee,
Are scars to the careless beholder
   And blemishes. So it may be;
But every such blemish endorses
   The pluck of a steed unafraid,
And the heart of a lover of horses
   Goes out to the Battered Brigade.

Their line is the line of the foxes,
    Their pace is the pace of the pack,
Though tomorrow they stand in their boxes
    As stiff as the props of a stack;
And I'll lay you my cheque at the banker's
    They're forward next week undismayed.
Good luck to the blemished front-rankers!
    Hats off to the Battered Brigade!

Their knocks have been gathered in duty,
    Their scars in the front of the fray;
It isn't your cleanest-legged beauty
    That's first at the end of the day.
When five foot of timber before us
    Has half of the pretty ones stayed,
If you want to catch up to the chorus
    Come on with the Battered Brigade!

Turned out in the finest of fettle,
    'Tis sometimes the soundest that fails,
And would rather hear hoofs on the metal
    Than follow the rattle of rails;
But out on the grass with hounds racing,
    And fences as big as they're made,
The cream of the gay steeple-chasing
    Is left to the Battered Brigade.

The Spotted Wonder

Steve Donoghue

Steve Donoghue was, in his day, the greatest of English jockeys. Not only was he a fine rider but he was a great horseman. They are not always the same thing. Some great horsemen have never been astride a horse; some fine riders have little understanding of the horse under them. But Donoghue was a horseman on the ground and atop a horse. He knew that horses were individuals as truly as people are, and he never forgot that. Because of this, his stories of the great horses he has ridden have something not often found in stories of the turf. No horse he had known intimately was merely a bay of sixteen hands, with a blaze, but a real individual, almost a person.

The horse he writes of here was one of the fastest that ever lived. In England such horses are always suspect, for great speed and real stamina, so greatly admired there, are seldom found together. In this country the same is often true but there are exceptions. If Man o' War had not raced at three, there are many that would not believe he could have won over the distances requiring stamina. He, like The Tetrarch, had to go to the front at once and brooked no restraint. But once in a century, or maybe not that often, a horse comes along that is cast in a mold not quite of this earth. All the rules go by the board. Such horses can do everything and with ease. It is quite possible that this spotted gray was from this mold. Apparently Donoghue thought so. (–From Donoghue Up!*)*

The fastest horse I ever rode was The Tetrarch, and in some ways he was the greatest horse I have ever known. He was the nearest thing to a bullet in animal shape that I ever met.

"He was big, strong, but his color was gray—a rare and unpopular color in those days—and he had weird white blotches on him that made him look something like an enormous edition of a child's rocking-horse."

I have ridden a great number of fast sprinters—I could name a dozen of them—but I have never ridden a horse with anything approaching The Tetrarch's amazing speed. He was a phenomenon. He was something that our courses had not seen or heard of before—a freak.

It would require a book in itself to tell the full story of The Tetrarch as he appeared to me, the man who rode him in all his races and all his important gallops, but I can give you here some idea of his powerful personality, his immense speed and his curious character quite easily.

This is my impression of him. I saw him in the sale-ring when Mr. "Atty" Persse, a brilliant and shrewd judge, bought him for thirteen hundred pounds, and most people thought that his judgment had slipped for once.

The horse was big, strong, but his color was gray—a rare and unpopular color in those days—and he had weird white blotches on him that made him look something like an enormous edition of a child's rocking-horse.

But leaving behind the sales-ring picture, and thinking of him purely as I knew him when he first went into training at Stockbridge, I can only say that this tremendous two-year-old looked a four-year-old, like a young hunter.

His quarters were immense; his muscular development was tremendous, and his length of rein caught your eye at once.

But apart from the extraordinary physical impressiveness of the colt, he had enormous personality. He commanded your respect and attention no matter what he did.

He certainly had been on this earth before. From the day he first had his breaking tack on he knew his business. He knew everything there was to know about racing the first time I took him on to a course. I will never forget that first occasion. It happened during the first Newmarket Spring Meeting, and the race for which the horse ran was the Maiden Two-Year-Old Plate.

The night before the race I stayed with my old friend Whalley with his father and mother at Red House. During the evening he told me that he was riding a really good horse the following day in the Plate. After a minute or two we discovered that he was running in the same race as was The Tetrarch.

Whalley told me that his horse's name was Mount William and that he was certain to win. He had been out already that season—though it was only then April—and he had won the Beckhampton 2-Y.-o. Plate at Newbury in a manner that made hacks of his opponents. Now Mr. Persse had galloped The Tetrarch at Chattis Hill, his training quarters, against horses and carrying weights that told us that there was not the slightest possible doubt he was a wonder, a freak.

Confident in the brilliant ability of my horse, though it was his first visit to a racecourse, I spent most of the evening pulling Whalley's leg. I told him that I was riding a horse that would make his appear slow. He could not think of Mount William being defeated. "I am riding an odd-colored beggar tomorrow, Snowy," I told him. "But he can go a bit. I think he'll make your horse gallop." Whalley laughed at me. I did not say much, because we were keeping quiet about the gray.

Well, the afternoon came on. My instructions were to canter steady to the post.

As a matter of fact, had the public seen him stretching himself on the way to the post his price would not have been five to one. His stride was so immense and impressive that even the general public would have realized that he was the exceptional horse.

I was just hack-cantering the horse down when I heard someone shout, "Say Steve, what are you ringin' in on us? Is that a four-year-old you're puttin' over on us?" It was Skeets Martin, the American jockey.

"No, he's a two-year-old," I answered. "He's a comical-looking fellow, isn't he?"

"Damn it, that horse is not a two-year-old, Steve," he insisted. Then I saw "Snowy" Whalley. "Snowy," I said to him, "that is the horse I was talking about. Have a look at those quarters."

"He certainly has some quarters, Steve," he said, a bit puzzled by the size and power of The Tetrarch.

"Well, that is all you will see of him in the race," I replied.

Mr. Persse had been very anxious about the horse's behavior at the starting gate. He had faced it only once at his training quarters. I had no fears. The horse knew his game inside out. I was only a little nervous that he would beat the gate.

We were drawn next to Whalley on Mount William as it happened. The Tetrarch set himself, watched the tapes and flashed out of the gate like a rocket.

I led by such a distance that there were moments when I wondered if there had actually been a false start. Mount William, with Whalley up was second, but a long way behind.

The horse's name was made that afternoon. No one had seen a horse with that electrical speed.

The next race he ran was in the Woodcote Stakes at Epsom. I cantered him down along the rails—I always used to do that as it teaches a horse the way to come back during the race—forgetting that two-year-old course was round the turn, I cantered straight on past the corner when I heard someone shout to me.

I then realized that I would have to bring this powerful horse around Tattenham corner. Gosh! The thought worried me for a moment. "How am I going to take this big fellow round that bend?" I asked myself.

But, as I have said, he had been on this earth before. As before he flashed out of the gate, in a few strides he headed his field, took the rails, and went round that corner as though he had been doing it all his life.

Next came Ascot. Once more he shot from the gate like a bullet, and though I saw the advance flag The Tetrarch's speed was so terrific that in a short while I could neither see nor hear anything near me and I thought there might have been a false start. I won by a tremendous margin and was actually in the paddock when the others were finishing their race.

I swear that horse had been on earth in a previous existence. He knew all about it. I shall not bother to tell the details of all his races. The first five he won in a manner that made his opponents appear absurd.

Then came a race about which I can speak with greater authority than anyone. It was at Sandown and a thick mist overhung the course. The time came when I found myself facing the starting gate on this unbeaten and sensationally fast horse.

The enclosures were crowded with people who had come specially to see the wonder horse.

Now The Tetrarch was always on the alert at the start and I was always afraid he might beat the gate some day, and sure enough this was the day he selected.

This time the luck was against him. He jumped off to a false start and in doing so got the tapes caught in his mouth. This caused him to rear up in the air. On coming down he landed on the quarters of the animal next to him and came down on his knees.

The significance of the happening soon swept through the heads of the quick-witted jockeys who were riding other horses in the race. A sort of murmur went through them: "The Tetrarch's down," and off they set like birds.

I was nearly heart-broken. Thousands of people had come down on this Bank Holiday to see the great horse, and here was I at the start with my horse all unbalanced and the field galloping away as fast as they could.

We had been cheered as he and I went down to the post—Brown Jack and Diadem were the only other horses I can remember evoking applause before a race—and here we were enmeshed in the tapes and the field rapidly disappearing out of sight.

I got The Tetrarch balanced and set off along after the leaders. I had little hope of catching them, as they were at the two-furlong post when I got the great horse balanced. I let him go, and I allowed him to make his own gallop.

I knew that to attempt to push him along, show him the whip or generally impose my will on him would be disastrous. He went after the field like a swallow and won the race by a neck on the post! It was his most wonderful performance.

But the general public who had come to adore the fantastic horse could not understand what had happened. They merely knew that the great horse whom they expected to win by streets just managed to scramble home a winner at all.

I was sorry for the great horse. It was not the distance he had to make up; it was the disappointment of being caught in the tapes.

The mist had been so thick that no one understood what had happened to the horse. As a matter of fact, and historically, this may be of interest. I think Mr. Persse, who trained the horse, mistrusted my judgment.

Persse had the idea in his clever head that quite possibly the horse had gone stale. I told him what had happened at the tapes, but my assessment of the race obviously did not seem to count with him this time.

Mr. Persse, not being able to see through the mist to the starting gate, and having seen his great horse just win by a neck, really believed that possibly the edge of speed had gone off his two-year-old.

I explained what had happened, but I knew he had his own views. We galloped the horse at home a day or so later, and that was the only time in his career that I let the wonderful gray really go full speed.

I was so determined that Persse should see that his suspicions about the horse having reached his zenith were false that I sent him along for the first time in his life.

He left the carefully weighted opposition as though they were hacks. Mr. Persse then understood and my knowledge of the incident was supported.

On he went through his unbeaten career. The best horses in England were put up against him and he left them standing.

He was the strangest creature. He could not stand being held back or made to wait. No, he would dash off in front and nothing on four legs could keep with him. But you could not wait with him.

I tried it but the horse did not go when called upon to do so, as he went when allowed to go out in front.

He won his seven two-year-old races easily, and he was spoken of as the automatic favorite for the following year's Derby. There was a lot of talk about his inability to stay because of his pedigree and his terrific speed. That will never be truly known. He could have won the Two Thousand Guineas, but his trainer did not allow him to run. Persse was very careful not to let the horse run unless he was perfectly well and fit. He was right, of course.

I offered, because I knew what a powerful horse he was for the lads to control and the fact that he had rapped himself a time or two, to give up my rides at Newmarket and stay with the horse to ride him in his gallops.

Mr. Persse, however, said it would be better for me to ride him at Newmarket. While there we got a wire saying he had rapped himself badly and injured himself in his work. Mr. Persse scratched him from the Derby.

The Tetrarch might have won the Derby by reason of his great speed.

Now, when The Tetrarch was scratched from the Derby, to the disappointment of many people, his owner resolved not to run him any more. A year or so later he was sent to the stud. At the stud, though he was a most unprolific sire, he had a vastly more important influence on our racing stock than all his seven victories.

He got 130 foals in about twenty years, and eighty of them were winners of races worth roughly one hundred seventy-five thousand pounds.

But even that is no measure of his greatness. Though the tribe he fathered were small their influence on the breed of racehorse has been immense.

We will probably never see his like on our racecourses again, but if we see something resembling him that something will probably be one of his own descendants. He was a wonder.

The Tetrarch was without the least doubt the fastest horse that I ever rode, and probably the fastest horse that ever ran on our turf. He had not the gentle good-fellowship of Brown Jack or the grace of other great horses I have ridden.

He was a great and imposing individual, and he had to have his own way.

Brown Jack

Steve Donoghue

"I find it hard to think of Brown Jack as a horse, he was so much more," wrote Steve Donoghue of his hero, and as the story of this amazing individual unfolds, we can easily see why. Many turf heroes are admired but none won the affection of the crowds as did Brown Jack. (−From Donoghue Up!*)*

I find it hard to write of Brown Jack as though he were an ordinary horse, or even a horse at all. He was so much more. If you try to think of a perfect gentleman with a few strange and particular little habits of his own, that is Brown Jack.

He was the most delightfully-mannered old gentleman you could wish to meet. He was also the gamest, most intelligent, and generous horse that ever looked through a bridle.

We became friends from the first moment we came together. It is strange that we ever did come together. A lot of people do not know that Brown Jack was the champion hurdler of the country before he had ever run on the flat. It is my belief that he would have won the Grand National if he had been entered for it.

I had just returned from a winter abroad when the Hon. Aubrey Hastings, one of the greatest horsemen and trainers that ever lived, said to me:

"I want you to see a horse of mine which is running in the Champion Hurdle today. I want to know if you think he would do well on the flat. Come and have a look at him." The horse won.

I told Hastings the horse was a real good one and would certainly do well on the flat.

Not long afterwards he was entered for a mile and three-quarters

"I find it hard to write of Brown Jack as though he were an ordinary horse, or even a horse at all. He was so much more."

at Hurst Park and I rode Brown Jack for the first time. I fell in love with him on the spot.

He did not win the race; in fact, he barely tried to win it. It was a new game to him and he did not understand what it was all about. He kept cocking one ear and then the other; he gazed ahead in a puzzled way and I expected him to turn to me and ask, "Hey, Steve, what sort of a race is this? When are we coming to the jumps? Are you sure we're on the right course? I've never been in a race without jumps before."

The intelligent fellow was working it all out for himself!

That one race had taught me what a genuine, game animal he was. His next race was a mile and a half at Windsor. He gave me a real taste of his courage in that race. He battled out the last furlong like a lion and won by a head. He was still a bit green, but his pluck saved him, although I felt the race was too short for such a real stayer.

Next time out Hastings took him to Kempton and ran him over two miles, and again he won by his old-fashioned head.

Well, Jack had shown what he could do. We all thought it over and it was decided to give him a chance at Ascot.

We had done well enough in our prep schools, now we would have a look over the public school. As the old lad went down to the post for the Ascot Stakes over two miles, he felt the place suited him down to the ground. There were twenty-one of us at the starting gate, and Jack seemed to get on all right. He behaved perfectly; took his place and waited for the gate to go up. We got off nicely, slipped along at our own pace—rather fast.

I could feel that the old fellow was anxious to make a good impression among the silk hats. He knew he was not quite out of the same drawer, but also he knew the sort of thing they liked. We won just as we liked, by three lengths.

For a moment I thought Jack intended to go around again. But he stopped eventually.

As we went back to weigh in Jack was very pleased with himself and I could see that he liked Ascot and would like to come here again.

From that moment onwards Jack made Ascot his own gallop. He had won the first time he galloped on the royal course and he won for the next six years in succession. The following year he really did show them what a lion he was.

He turned out for the same Ascot Stakes, but this time against some rattling good horses—and he was carrying top weight and giving away well over 2 stone (28 pounds) to most of them. He ran a wonderful race and was just beaten.

Three days later, as though that had been just an exercise gallop, he came out for the Alexandra Stakes, the longest race in the calendar, run over 2 miles, 6 furlongs and 75 years. He went along very nicely, a bit sharp because it was Ascot still, and we won as you like by four lengths. Not so bad in four days.

That was the first of six successive wins in that race, and we enjoyed them all.

Through all those six years Jack was a wonderful old fellow. It was just sheer happiness being with him.

We understood each other perfectly. I knew what a genuine old battler he was. It was he who got himself ready and it was he who ran his own races. Towards the end of a long race Jack would come up to the leaders in his own way. He would go alongside the first and sort of say to him, "Come along, lad, let's see what you can do." And he would go alongside that fellow, faster and faster, until he felt the other give way and fall back.

Then he would set out after the next one, and, when he had broken all their hearts, he would do his little dance, prick his ears, and expect me to pull him up. Often he did this a good way from the post, and I had to tell him to get on with it until he had finished. He understood, and the minute we passed the post he would repeat his little dance, prick his ears, and make for the paddock.

But early in the season Jack was an entirely different person. He used to spend the winter out at grass with an old carthorse friend of his, and when he was first put into work he took life in a very leisurely way. All day he would snooze, sitting on the manger, and his door wide open at the top. He never went down to rest in the straw, the iron manger was his hammock and he didn't like the door closed.

When Aubrey Hastings died and Ivor Anthony conducted the stables at Shrewton for Mrs. Hastings, Ivor, with his beautiful understanding of the old horse, had some soft leather put on the edge of the manger so that it would be softer on the old gentleman.

During the night Jack pulled it off with his teeth. Thinking that perhaps the job had been a bit amateurish and was not smooth enough, Ivor had a professional do the job. Again Jack pulled it off.

He liked a cool iron manger to sit on and none of your fussy leather ones, and that was that.

But he was very much a gentleman, and the time came when he consented to use a sort of a hammock and having tried it, he got to like it.

Jack had no fancy for hard work on the gallops of a morning. No, no, he liked to warm to his work slowly and steadily.

He would saunter along nicely, but no real galloping. Then he would be entered for a nice mile and a half race at some place like Nottingham; nobody expected him to win, he was just getting a feel of the course on his feet.

Now Jack had rather thin-soled feet and he didn't like the going too hard. At Nottingham he would go down to the post a bit tenderly and say to me, "Steady, now, Steve, don't ask too much. The old feet are not so good and this going is horribly hard. I'll give you a nice little gallop but don't ask for too much. Steady, now."

But towards Ascot time we had to ask the old lad to step along a bit, and if you asked him the right way he would be very generous. Of course, he would not consent to do any work on the home gallops. Oh, no, he put the bar up to any nonsense like that. The thing had to be organized properly.

Horseboxes would drive into the yard, Old Mail Fist, Jack's companion, would be put into one, and Jack into another. There would be plenty of fuss and noise, and all the appearance of a racing day, and the old gentlemen would be driven miles away over to Lambourn or Beckhampton, or some other strange gallop.

I would arrive down by car, and when Jack saw me coming along all dressed up for a race he would get ready to stretch himself a little. But if he suspected that he was being fooled, or if I wasn't there, he would chuckle to himself and doddle along just as though he were at home.

Gordon Richards went down to ride him a gallop one day and it didn't work. Champion jockey or no champion jockey, Jack smelt that something was wrong. Gordon could not get the old fellow out of a canter. He tried every trick he knew and then rode over to the trainer, shrugged his shoulders, and said, "It wants two jockeys to get this old lad to do anything. I can't manage him, I'm exhausted trying."

But later when I turned up and he realized that the "guv'nor" was about, he went off like a perfect gentleman.

Yet when Jack was really ready for Ascot—which was the aim of all the earlier races—things were different. By then he had worked himself into condition and he rather enjoyed a gallop, but until he was feeling that way he would not allow himself to be knocked about.

That was why he was as good a horse at ten years as he had been as the four-year-old champion hurdler. I loved the old fellow like a brother; I rode him in forty races and dismounted from him the last time leaving him as fresh and youthful as when I had first met him. We understood each other perfectly.

He had a light heart and everything he did in his own humorous way made me love him more. He gave me the proudest, the happiest, the most triumphant days of my life. I love horses with all that is in me. Their speed and courage and affection have enabled me to rise from nothing to enjoy a wonderful career. Some people think of them as animals—I think of them as friends, my greatest friends.

There was never one with whom I was associated who brought me greater joy than gallant Brown Jack and his old-fashioned ways. Not a day passes but I think of him, and I know then how rich are my memories.

Ole Man Sanford

John Taintor Foote

John Taintor Foote was a Kentuckian who was trained as an artist. He began a career in commercial art, but abandoned it to begin writing horse stories, which were immediately successful. This story and the one following first appeared in the Saturday Evening Post *in the early nineteen hundreds when the* Post *was the most success-ful magazine of its kind. These stories deal with racing of another day; before the saliva test eliminated stimulation of horses, before pari mutuel betting and before big purses became a commonplace thing. That the author knew and loved horses is apparent in every line and paragraph. (–From* Hoofbeats)

Do you happen to notice a old duck that comes to the stalls at Loueyville just after the derby?" asked Blister.

"Was his name Sanford, and did he wish to pat the mare?" I asked in turn.

"That's him," said Blister. "Ole man Sanford. It ain't likely you ever heard of him, but everybody on the track knows him, if they ever hit the Loueyville meetin'. They never charge him nothin' to get into the gates. He ain't a owner no more, but way back there before I'm alive he wins the Kentucky Derby with Sweet Alice, 'n' from what I hears she was a grand mare. Ole man Sanford breeds Sweet Alice hisself. In them days he's got a big place not far from Loueyville. They tell me his folks get the land original from the govanment when it's nothin' but timber. I hears once, but it don't hardly sound reasonable, that they hands over a half a million acres to the first ole man Sanford, who was a granddaddy of this ole man

"Of all the horses who have been a glory to our state, suh, but one otheh had as game a heart as this superb creature."

Sanford. If that's so, Uncle Sam was more of a sport in them days than since.

"I don't know how they pry it all loose from him, but one mawnin' ole man Sanford wakes up clean as a whistle. They've copped the whole works—he ain't got nothin'. He goes to keepin' books fur a whiskey house in Loueyville, 'n' he holds the job down steady fur twenty years. The only time he quits pen-pushin' is when they race at Churchill Downs. From the first minute the meetin' opens till getaway day comes he's bright eyes at the rat hole. He don't add up no figgers fur nobody then. He just putters around the track. He's doped out as sorta harmless by the bunch.

"After the Très Jolie mare wins the derby fur me, ole man Sanford makes my stalls his hangout. I ain't kickin', all he wants to do is to look at the mare 'n' chew the rag about her. That satisfies him completely.

" 'Of all the hawsses, suh, who have been a glory to our state', he says, 'but one otheh had as game a heart as this superb creature. I refer to Sweet Alice, suh,—a race mayah of such quality that the world marveled. Not in a boastful manner, suh, but with propah humility, let me say that I had the honor to breed and raise Sweet Alice, and that she bore my colors when she won the tenth renewal of our great classic.'

"He tells this to everybody that comes past the stalls, 'n' it ain't long till he begins to bring people around to look the mare over. From that he gets to watchin' how the swipes take care of her. Pretty soon he begins to call 'em if things ain't done to suit him.

" 'Boy,' he'll say, 'that bandage is tighter than I like to see it. Always allow the tendon a little play—do not impaieh the suhculation.'

"The boys eat this stuff up—it tickles 'em. They treat him respectful 'n' do what he tells 'em.

" 'Everything O.K. today, sir?' they'll say.

"Ole man Sanford don't tumble they're kiddin' him.

" 'Ah have nothing to complain of,' he says.

"It ain't long till he's overseein' my whole string of hosses, just like he owns 'em. Man, he sure does enjoy hisself. He won't trade places with August Belmont.

"I'm gettin' Trampfast ready fur a nice little killin'. He's finished away back in two starts, but he runs both races without a pill. This hoss is a dope. He's been on it fur two seasons. He won't beat nothin' without his hop. But when he gets just the right mixture under his hide he figgers he can beat any kind of a hoss, 'n' he's about right at that. He thinks he's a ragin' lion. He can't wait to go out there 'n' eat up them kittens that's goin' to start against him.

"One mawnin' my boy Pete takes the Trampfast hoss out fur a trial.

" 'If he'll go six furlongs in about fourteen,' I says to Pete, 'he's right. If he tries to loaf on you, shake him up; but if he's doin' his work nice, let him suit hisself 'n' keep the bat off him. I want to see what he'll do on his own.'

" 'I think he'll perform today,' says Pete. 'He's felt real good to me fur the last week.'

"Ole man Sanford standin' there listenin'. When the workout starts he ketches the time with a big gold stop clock that he fishes out of his shiny ole vest. The clock's old, too—it winds with a key—but at that she's a peach!

" 'That's a fine clock,' I says to him. He don't take his eyes off the hoss comin' round the bend.

" 'He's running with freedom and well within himself,' he says. 'That quatah was in twenty-foh flat! Yes, suh, this watch was presented to me by membahs of the Breedah's Association to commemorate the victory of Sweet Alice in the tenth renewal of our classic. You have heard me speak of Sweet Alice?'

" 'Yes, you told me about her, Mr. Sanford,' I says. 'That's sure some clock.'

" 'If he does not falteh in the stretch, suh,' says ole man Sanford, 'I will presently show you the one minute and fohteen seconds you desiah upon it's face.'

"The ole man's a good judge of pace,—Trampfast comes home bang in the fourteen notch.

"When Pete gets down at the stalls, ole man Sanford walks up to him.

" 'Hyah is a dollah foh you, boy,' he says, 'n' hands Pete a buck. 'That was a well-rated trial.'

"Pete looks at the silver buck 'n' then at ole man Sanford 'n' then at me.

" 'What the hell—,' he says.

" 'You rough neck!' I says to Pete. 'Don't you know how to act when a gentleman slips you somethin'?'

" 'But look a-here,' says Pete. 'He ain't got—' I gives Pete a poke in the slats. 'Much obliged, sir,' he says, 'n' puts the bone in his pocket.

" 'You are entirely welcome, mah boy,' says ole man Sanford, wavin' his hand.

" 'Say,' Pete says to me, 'I think this hoss'll cop without a shot in the arm. He's awful good!'

" 'Not fur mine,' I says. 'He can run fur Sweeney when he ain't got no hop in him. Just let some sassy hoss look him in the eye fur two jumps 'n' he'll holler, "Please, mister, don't!" Yea, bo',' I says, 'I know this pup too well. When he's carrying my kale he'll be shoutin' hallelooyah with a big joy pill under his belt.'

"I forgets all about ole man Sanford bein' there. You don't talk about hoppin' one with strangers listenin', but he's around so much I never thinks. All of a sudden he's standin' in front of me lookin' like there's somethin' hurtin' him.

" 'What's the matter, Mr. Sanford?' I says.

" 'I gathah from yoh convahsation,' says he, 'that it is yoh practice to supplement the fine courage God has given the thoroughbred with vile stimulants. Am I correct in this supposition, suh?'

" 'Why, yes—' I says, kinda took back. 'When they need it I sure gives it to 'em.'

"Ole man Sanford draws hisself up 'n' looks at me like I'm a toad.

" 'Suh,' he says, 'the man who does that degrades himself and the helpless creature that Providence has placed in his keeping! Not only that, suh, but he insults the name of the thoroughbred and all it stands for, still tendahly cherished by some of us. Ah have heard of this abhorrent practice that has come as a part of this mercenary age, and, suh, Ah abominate both it and the man who would be guilty of such an act!'

" 'Why, looka here, Mr. Sanford,' I says. 'They're all doin' it. If you're goin' to train hosses you've got to get in the band wagon. If *you* can't give the owner a run fur his money he'll find somebody to train 'em who can!'

" 'Do you mean to tell me, suh, the wonderful courage displayed by that mayah when the time came, was false?' says ole man Sanford, pointin' at Très Jolie's stall. 'Ah saw strong men, the backbone of this state, suh,' he says, 'watch that mayah come home with tears in their eyes. Were their natures moved to the depths by an insulting counterfeit of greatness?'

" 'Why, sure not.' I says. 'But all hosses ain't like her.'

" 'They are not, suh!' says ole man Sanford. 'Noh were they intended to be! But few of us are ordained foh the heights. However,' he says puttin' his hand on my shoulder, 'Ah should not censure you too strongly, young man. In fohcing yoh hawses to simulate qualities they do not possess, you are only a paht of yoh times. This is the day of imitation—I find it between the covahs of yoh book—I hear it in the music yoh applaud—I see it riding by in motahcars. Imitation—all imitation!'

"I ain't hep to this line of chatter—it's by me. But I dopes out he's sore at automobiles.

" 'What's wrong with 'em?' I says to him.

" 'Ah don't feel qualified to answer yoh question, suh,' he says. "Ah believe the blind pursuit and worship of riches is almost entirely responsible. It has bred a shallowness and superficiality in and towahds the finah things of life. But the historian will answer yoh question at a later day. He can bring calmness to the task which is impossible to one surrounded and bewildered by it all.'

"I ain't any wiser'n I was, but I don't say nothin'. The old man acts like he's studyin' about somethin'.

" 'Who owns the hawss that just trialed three-quatahs in foh-teen?' he says after awhile.

" 'Jim Sigsbee up at Cynthiana.' I says.

" 'Is Mr. Sigsbee awaheh of the—method you pursue with regahd to falsely stimulating his hawss?' says ole man Sanford.

" 'Well, I guess yes!' I says. 'Jim won't bet a dollar on him unless he's got the hop in him.'

" 'Ah shall write to him,' says ole man Sanford 'n' beats it down the track toward the gates.

"I don't see him fur over a week. I figger he's sore at me fur dopin' horses. It's a funny thing but I'm a son-of-a-gun if I don't miss the old duck. From the way they talk I see the boys kinda miss him too. 'I wonder where ole Pierpont's at?' I hears Chick ask Skinny. 'Gone East to see one of his hosses prepped fur the Brooklyn, I guess.'

" 'Naw,' says Skinny, 'you got that wrong. He's goin' to send a stable to Urope 'n' Todd Sloan's tryin' to get a contrac' from him as exercise boy. Ole Pierpont's watchin' Todd work out a few so he can size up his style.' . . .

"I've wrote Jim Sigsbee Trampfast's ready, but I don't enter the hoss 'cause I know Jim wants to come over 'n' bet a piece of money on him. I don't hear from Jim, 'n' I wonder why.

"One day I'm settin' in front of the stalls 'n' here comes ole man Sanford down the line.

" 'Why hello, Mr. Sanford!' I says. 'We sorta figgered you'd quit us. Things ain't gone right since you left. The boys need you to keep 'em on their toes.'

" 'Ah have not deserted you intentionally, suh,' he says. 'Since Ah saw you last an old friend of mine has passed to his rewahd. The Hono'able James Tullfohd Fawcett is no moh, suh.—a gallant gentleman has left us.'

" 'That's too bad,' I says. 'Did he leave a family?'

" 'He did not, suh,' says ole man Sanford. 'Ah fell heir to his entire estate, only excepting the silver mug presented to his beloved mothah at his birth by Andrew Jackson himself, suh. This he bequeathed to the public, and it will soon be displayed at the rooms of the Historical Society named in his last will and testament.'

" 'Did you get much out of it?' I says.

" 'He had already endowed me with a friendship beyond price,

"But, suh, the hawss will race on his merits and without any sort of stimulant."

suh,' he says. 'His estate was not a large one as such things go—
some twelve hundred dollahs, I believe.'

" 'That's better'n breakin' a leg,' I says.

" 'You will, perhaps, be interested to learn,' says he, 'that Ah
have pu'chased the hawss Trampfast with a po'tion of the money.
Hyah is a letter foh you from Mr. Sigsbee relative to the mattah.'
He hands me a letter, but I can't hardly read it—his buyin' this hop-
head gets my goat.

" 'What you goin' to do with him?' I says. 'Race him?'

" 'That is ma intention, suh,' he says. 'Ah expect to keep him in
yoh hands. But, of co'se, suh, the hawss will race on his merits and
without any sawt of stimulant.'

"I ain't stuck on the proposition. The Trampfast hoss can't beat a
cookstove without the hop. I hate to see the old man burn up his
dough on a dead one.

" 'Now, Mr. Sanford,' I says, 'times has changed since you raced.
If you let me handle this hoss to suit myself I think I can make a
piece of money fur you. The game ain't like it was once, 'n' if you
try to pull the stuff that got by thirty years ago, they'll trim you
right down to the suspenders. They ain't nothin' crooked about
slippin' the hop into a hoss that needs it.'

" 'As neahly as Ah can follow yoh fohm of speech,' says ole man
Sanford, 'you intend to convey the impression that the practice of
stimulating a hawss has become entirely propah. Am I correct,
suh?'

" 'That's it,' I says, ' 'n' you can gamble I'm right.'

" 'Is the practice allowed under present day racing rules?' says
ole man Sanford, ' 'n' I think I've got him goin'.

" 'Why, sure not,' I says, 'But how long would a guy last if he
never broke a racin' rule?'

" 'Out of yoh own mouth is yoh argument condemned, suh,' says
ole man Sanford. 'Even in this day and generation the rules fohbid
it—and let me say, suh, that should a trainah, a jockey, or anyone
connected with a stable of mine be guilty of wilfully violating a
racing rule, Ah would discharge him at once, suh!'

" '*You goin' to race on the level all the time?*' I says.

" 'If by that expression you mean hono'ably and as a gentleman—yes suh!'

" *'Good night, nurse!'* I says. 'You'll go broke quick at that game!'

" 'Allow me to remind you that that is ma own affaih, suh,' says ole man Sanford, 'n' the argument's over. His ideas date back so far they're mildewed, but I see I can't change 'em. He don't belong around a race track no more'n your grandmother.

" 'All right, Mr. Sanford,' I says. 'You're the doctor! We'll handle him just like you say.'

"Pewee Simpson has come over to chew the rag with me 'n' he hears most of this talk.

" 'Wait till I call the boys,' he says when ole man Sanford goes in to look at the hoss.

" 'What fur?' I says.

" 'Family prayers,' says Pewee.

"I throws a scraper at him, 'n' he goes on down the line singin' *Onward, Christian Soldiers.*

"Ole man Sanford orders a set of silks. He's got to send away fur the kind he wants 'n' he won't let me start the hoss till they come. Nobody but big stables pays attention to colors, so I tries to talk him out of the notion,—nothin' doin'!

" 'Mah colors were known and respected in days gone by, suh,' he says. 'Ah owe it to the public who reposed confidence in the puhple and white, to fly ma old flag when Ah once moh take the field. Yes suh.'

" 'Purple 'n' white!' I says. 'Them's the colors of the McVay stable!'

" 'Ah was breeding stake hawsses, suh,' say ole man Sanford, 'when his mothah's milk was not yet dry upon the lips of young McVay.'

"When the silks come, I pick out a real soft spot for Trampfast. It's a six furlong ramble fur has-beens 'n' there's sure a bunch of kioodles in it! Most of 'em ought to be on crutches. My hoss has showed me the distance in fourteen, 'n' that's about where this gang'll stagger home. With the hop in him the Trampfast hoss'll give me two seconds better. He ought to be a swell bet. But the hop puts all the heart in him there is—he ain't got one of his own. If he runs empty he'll lay down sure. I can't hop him, so I won't bet on him with counterfeit money.

"The mawnin' of the race ole man Sanford's at the stalls bright 'n' early. He's chipper as a canary. He watches Chick hand-rub the hoss fur a while 'n' then he pulls out a roll 'n' eases Chick two bucks. I pipes off the roll. The ole man sees me lookin' at it.

" 'Ah intends to wageh moderately today,' he says, 'And Ah have brought a small sum with me foh the puhpose.'

" 'What you goin' to bet on?' I says.

" 'Mah own hawss, of co'se, suh,' says he. 'It is mah custom to back only mah own hawsses or those of mah friends.'

"I don't say nothin'. I'm wise by this time, he plays the game to suit hisself, but it sure makes me sick. I hate as bad to see the ole man lose his dough as if it's mine.

"I goes over 'n' sets down on the track fence.

" 'When you train a hoss fur a guy you do like he says, don't you?' I says to myself. 'You don't own this hoss, 'n' the owner doesn't want him hopped. They ain't but one answer—don't hop him.'

" 'But looka here,' I says back to myself, 'If you sees a child in wrong, you tell him to beat it, don't you? It ain't your child, is it? Well, this ole man ain't nothin' but a child. If he was, he'd let you hop the hoss 'n' make a killin' fur him.' I argues with myself this way, but they can't neither of us figger it out to suit the other.

"I wish the damned old fool had somebody else a-trainin' his dog. I thinks after I've set there a hour 'n' ain't no further along 'n' I was when I starts.

"When it's gettin' along towards post time, ole man Sanford hikes fur the stand.

" 'Skinny,' I says, 'amble over to the bettin' shed 'n' watch what the ole man does. As soon as he's got his kale down, beat it back here on the jump 'n' tell me how much he gets on 'n' what the odds are.'

"In about ten minutes here comes Skinny at a forty shot.

" 'He bets a hundred straight at fifteen to one! What do you know about that?' he hollers.

" 'That settles it!' I says. 'Chick get them two bottles that's hid under the rub rags in the trunk! Now, ole Holler-enough,' I says to the Tramp, 'you may be a imitation hoss, but we're goin' to make you look so much like the real thing your own mother won't know you! . . .'

"When Trampfast starts fur the paddock, his eyes has begun to roll 'n' he's walkin' proud.

" 'He thinks he's the Zar Of Rushy,' says Chick. 'He'll be seein' pink elephants in a minute.'

"I don't find ole man Sanford till they're at the post. He's standin' by the fence at the wire.

"The start's bein' held up by the Tramp. He's sure puttin' on a show—the hop's got him as wild as a eagle. It's too far away fur the ole man to see good, so I don't put him hep it's his hoss that's cuttin' the didoes.

"Just then Chick comes up.

" 'I hear you get a nice bet down on your hoss, Mr. Sanford,' he says. 'I sure hope he cops.'

" 'Thank you, ma boy,' says ole man Sanford. 'I only placed a small wageh but at vehy liberal odds. Ah shall profit materially should he win his race.'

" 'If he gets away good he'll roll,' says Chick. 'There's no class to that bunch, 'n' he's a bear with a shot in him. But he's a bad actor when he's hopped—look at the fancy stuff he's pullin' now!'

" 'You are mistaken, ma boy,' says ole man Sanford. 'This hawss has had no stimulant *today.*'

"Like a nut I furgot to tell the boys the ole man ain't on. I tries to give Chick the high sign, but he's watchin' the hosses 'n' before I can get to him he belches up the glad news.

" 'If *he* ain't hopped one never was!' he says. 'We put a fierce shot in him. Look at him act if you don—'

"I kick his shin off right there, but it's too late, ole man Sanford gets pale as a rag.

" 'How dare you—' he says, 'n' stops. 'But ah shall prevent it!' he says, 'n' starts fur the judges stand. He ain't got a chance—just then they get away 'n' he turns back to me when he hears the crowd holler, 'They're off!'

" 'Young man,' he says, pointin' at me, 'n' he's shakin' like he's cold. 'What have Ah evah done to you to merit such treatment at yoh hands?'

"I see there's no use to lie to him, so I gives it to him straight.

" 'Mr. Sanford,' I says, 'the hoss can't win without it, 'n' I don't want to see you lose your money.'

"Ole man Sanford sorta wilts. He seems to get smaller. I've never noticed how old he is till now. He stands a-lookin' at me like he never sees me before.

"The crowd begins to yell as the hosses hit the stretch. The Tramp is out in front 'n' he stays there all the way. The ole man never even looks towards the track.

" 'He wins easy,' says Chick as they go under the wire, 'n' all you can hear is 'Trampfast! Trampfast!' but ole man Sanford still keeps a-starin' at me.

" 'You want to cheer up, Mr. Sanford,' I says. 'You win a nice bet on him.'

"He pulls the tickets out of his pocket 'n' looks at 'em. They call fur sixteen hundred bucks.

" 'As Ah have told you once befoh, young man,' he says, a-lookin' at the tickets, 'Ah can not blame you greatly, because you are paht of your times. This is the excuse Ah find foh you in thinking Ah would value money moh than the spohtsmanship of a gentleman. Yoh times are bad, young man!' he says. 'They have succeeded in staining the puhple and white at the vehy end. Ah would nevah have raced afteh today. It was a whim of an old man to see his colohs once more among a field of hawsses. Ah knew Ah was not of this day. Ah should have known bettah than to become a paht of it even foh a little time. Ah have learned ma lesson,' he says, lookin' up at me. 'But you have made it vehy bittah.'

"He looks down at his tickets again fur a minute. . . . Then he tears 'em across three ways 'n' drops 'em on the ground."

The Look of Eagles

John Taintor Foote

This story is a kind of sequel to the previous story. I consider it one of the very best horse stories ever written. (—From Hoofbeats)

I had waited ten minutes on that corner. At last I ventured out from the curb and peered down the street, hoping for the sight of a red and white sign that read: THIS CAR FOR THE RACES. Then a motor horn bellowed, too close for comfort. I stepped back hastily in favor of the purring giant that bore it, and looked up into the smiling eyes of the master of Thistle Ridge. The big car slid its length and stopped. Its flanks were white with dust. Its little stint that morning had been to sweep away the miles between Lexington and Louisville.

"Early, aren't you?" asked Judge Dillon as I settled back contentedly at his side.

"Thought I'd spend a few hours with our mutual friend," I explained.

I felt an amused glance.

"Diverting and—er—profitable, eh? What does the victim say about it?"

"He never reads them," I confessed; and Judge Dillon chuckled.

"I've come over to see our Derby candidate in particular," he informed me. "I haven't heard from him for a month. Your friend is a poor correspondent."

The gateman at Churchill Downs shouted directions at us a few moments later and the car swung to the left, past a city of stables. As we wheeled through a gap in a line of whitewashed stalls we heard the raised voice of Blister Jones. He was confronting the hapless Chick and a steaming bucket.

93

"Fur the brown stud, eh?" we heard. "Let's look at it."

Chick presented the bucket in silence. Blister peered at its contents.

"Soup!" he sniffed. "I thought so. Go rub it in your hair."

"You tells me to throw the wet feed into him, didn't you?" Chick inquired defensively.

"Last week—yes," said Blister. "Not all summer. Someday a thought'll get in your nut 'n' bust it!" His eye caught the motor and his frown was instantly blotted out.

"Why, how-de-do, Judge!" he said. "I didn't see you."

"Don't mind us," Judge Dillon told him as we alighted. "How's the colt?"

Blister turned and glanced at a shining bay head protruding from an upper door.

"Well, I'll tell you," he said deliberately, "he ain't such a bad sort of a colt in some ways. Fur a while I liked him; but here lately I get to thinkin' he won't do. He's got a lot of step. He shows me a couple o' nice works; but if he makes a stake hoss I'm fooled bad."

"Huh!" grunted Judge Dillon. "What's the matter? Is he sluggish?"

"That wouldn't worry me so much if he was," said Blister. "They don't have to go speed crazy all at once." He hesitated for a moment, looking up into the owner's face. Then, as one breaking terrible news: "Judge," he said, "he ain't got the class."

There followed a silence. In it I became aware that the blue and gold of Thistle Ridge would not flash from the barrier on Derby Day.

"Well, ship him home," said Judge Dillon at last as he sat down rather heavily on a bale of hay. He glanced once at the slim bay head, then turned to us with a smile. "Better luck next year," he said.

I was tongue-tied before that smile, but Blister came to the rescue.

"You still like that Fire Fly cross, don't you?" he asked with a challenge in his voice.

"I do," asserted Judge Dillon firmly. "It gives 'em bone like nothing else."

"Yep," agreed Blister, " 'n' a lot of it goes to the head. None of that Fire Fly blood fur mine. Nine out of ten of 'em sprawl. They don't gather up like they meant it. Now you take ole Torch Bearer—"

I found a chair and became busy with my own thoughts. I wondered if, after all, the breeding of speed horses was not too cruelly disappointing to those whose heart and soul were in it. The moments of triumph were wonderful, of course. The thrill of any other game was feeble in comparison; but oh, the many and bitter disappointments!

At last I became conscious of a little old man approaching down the line of stalls. His clothes were quite shabby; but he walked with crisp erectness, with something of an air. He carried his soft hat in his hand and his silky hair glistened like silver in the sunshine. As he stopped and addressed a stable boy, a dozen stalls from where we sat, the courteous tilt of his head was vaguely familiar.

"Who's that old man down there?" I asked. "I think I've seen him before."

Blister followed my eyes and sat up in his chair with a jerk. He looked about him as though contemplating flight.

"Oh Lord!" he said. "Now I'll get mine!"

"Who is it?" I repeated.

"Ole Man Sanford," answered Blister. "I ain't seen him fur a year. I hopped a hoss for him once. I guess I told you."

I nodded.

"What's he talking about?" asked Judge Dillon.

And I explained how Old Man Sanford, a big breeder in his day, was now in reduced circumstances; how he had, with a small legacy, purchased a horse and placed him in Blister's hands; how Blister had given the horse stimulants before a race, contrary to racing rules; and how Mr. Sanford had discovered it and had torn up his tickets when the horse won.

"Tore up his tickets!" exclaimed Judge Dillon. "How much?"

"Fifteen hundred dollars," I replied. "All he had in the world."

Judge Dillon whistled.

"I've met him," he said. "He won a Derby thirty years ago." He bent forward and examined the straight, white-haired little figure. "Tore up his tickets, eh?" he repeated. Then softly: "Blood will tell!"

"Here he comes," said Blister uneasily. "He'll give me the once-over 'n' brush by, I guess."

But Old Man Sanford did nothing of the sort. A radiant smile and two extended hands greeted Blister's awkward advance.

"My deah young friend, how is the world treatin' you these days?"

"Pretty good, Mr. Sanford," answered Blister and hesitated. "I kinda thought you'd be sore at me," he confessed. "While I didn't mean it that way, I give you a raw deal, didn't I?"

A hand rested on Blister's sleeve for an instant.

"When yoh hair," said Old Man Sanford, "has taken it's color from the many wintuhs whose stohms have bowed yoh head, you will have learned this: We act accohdin' to our lights. Some are brighter, some are dimmer, than others; but who shall be the judge?"

Whether or not Blister got the finer shadings of this, the sense of it was plain.

"I might have knowed you wouldn't be sore," he said relieved. "Here's Chick. You remember Chick, Mr. Sanford."

Chick was greeted radiantly. Likewise "Petah."

"And the hawses? How are the hawses? Have you a nice string?" Blister turned and "made us acquainted" with Old Man Sanford.

"Chick," he called, "get a chair fur Mr. Sanford. Pete—you boys start in with the sorrel hoss 'n' bring 'em all out, one at a time!"

"Why, now," said Mr. Sanford, "I mustn't make a nuisance of myself. It would be a great pleasuh, suh, to see yoh hawses; but I do not wish to bothah you. Suppose I just walk from stall to stall?"

He tried to advance toward the stalls, but was confronted by Blister, who took him by the arms, smiled down into his face, and gave him a gentle shake.

"Now listen!" said Blister. "As long as we're here you treat this string like it's yours. They'll come out 'n' stand on their ears if you want to see it. You got me?"

I saw a dull red mount slowly to the wrinkled cheeks. The little figure became straighter, if possible, in its threadbare black suit. I saw an enormous silk handkerchief, embroidered and yellow with age, appear suddenly as Old Man Sanford blew his nose. He started to speak, faltered, and again was obliged to resort to the handkerchief.

"I thank you, suh," he said at last, and found a chair as Judge Dillon's eyes sought mine.

We left him out of our conversation for a time; but as the string was led before him one by one the horseman in Mr. Sanford triumphed. He passed loving judgment on one and all, his face keen and lighted. Of the colt I had just heard doomed he said:

"A well-made youngsteh, gentlemen; his blood speaks in every line of him. But as I look him oveh I have a feeling—it is, of cohse, no moh than that—that he lacks a certain quality essential to a great hawse."

"What quality?" asked Judge Dillon quickly.

"A racin' heart, suh," came the prompt reply.

"Oh, that's it, is it?" said Judge Dillon, and added dryly: "I own him."

Mr. Sanford gave one reproachful glance at Blister.

"I beg yoh pahdon, suh," he said earnestly to Judge Dillon. "A snap judgment in matters of this sawt is, of cohse, wo'thless. Do not give my words a thought, suh. They were spoken hastily, without due deliberation, with no real knowledge on which to base them. I sincerely hope I have not pained you, suh."

Judge Dillon's big hand swung over and covered one of the thin knees encased in shiny broadcloth.

"No sportsman," he said, "is ever hurt by the truth. That's just exactly what's the matter with him. But how did you know it?"

Mr. Sanford hesitated.

"I'm quite likely to be mistaken, suh," he said; "but if it would interest you I may say that I missed a certain look about his head, and moh pahticularly in his eyes, that is the hallmark—this is merely my opinion, suh—of a really great hawse."

"What kind of a look?" I asked.

Again Mr. Sanford hesitated.

"It is hard to define, suh," he explained. "It is not a matter of skull structure—of confohmation. It is—" He sought for words. "Well, suh, about the head of a truly great hawse there is an air of freedom unconquerable. The eyes seem to look on heights beyond our gaze. It is the look of a spirit that can soar. It is not confined to hawses; even in his pictures you can see it in the eyes of the Bonaparte. It is the birthright of eagles. They all have it—But I express myself badly." He turned to Judge Dillon. "Yoh great mayeh has it, suh, to a marked degree."

"Très Jolie?" inquired Judge Dillon, and Mr. Sanford nodded.

I had heard of a power—psychic, perhaps,—which comes to a few, a very few, who give their lives and their hearts to horses. I looked curiously at the little old man beside me. Did those faded watery eyes see something hidden from the rest of us? I wondered.

Blister interrupted my thoughts.

"Say, Mr. Sanford," he asked suddenly, "what did you ever do with Trampfast?"

"I disposed of him, suh, foh nine hundred dollahs."

Blister considered this for a moment.

"Look-a-here!" he said. "You don't like the way I handled that hoss fur you, 'n' I'd like a chance to make good. I know where I can buy a right good plater fur nine hundred dollars. I'll make him pay his way or no charge. What do you say?"

Mr. Sanford shook his head. "As a matteh of fact," he stated, "I have only six hundred dollahs now in hand. Aside from having learned that my racing methods are not those of today, I would not care to see the puhple and white on a six-hundred-dollah hawse."

"Why, look-a-here!" urged Blister. "All the big stables race platers. There's good money in it when it's handled right. Let a goat chew dust a few times till you can drop him in soft somewheres, 'n' then put a piece of change on him at nice juicy odds. The boy kicks a win out of him, maybe; 'n' right there he don't owe you nothin'.' "

Once more I saw a dull red flare up in Mr. Sanford's face; but now he favored Blister with a bristling stare.

"I have difficulty in following you at times, suh," he said. "Am I justified in believing that the word 'goat' is applied to a thoroughbred race hawse?"

"Why yes, Mr. Sanford," said Blister, "that's what I mean, I expect."

The old gentleman seemed to spend a moment in dismissing his wrath. When he spoke at last no trace of it was in his voice.

"I am fond of you, my young friend," he said. "Under a cynical exterior I have found you courteous, loyal, tender-hearted; but I deplore in you the shallow flippancy of this age. It is the fashion to sneer at the finer things; and so you call a racin' thoroughbred a goat. He is not of stakes quality, perhaps." Here the voice became quite gentle; "Are you?"

"I guess not, Mr. Sanford," admitted Blister.

"Never mind, my boy. If man breeds one genius to a decade it is enough. And so it goes with hawses. Foh thirty years, with love, with reverence, I tried to breed great hawses—hawses that would be a joy, an honoh to my state. In those days ninety colts were foaled each spring at Sanfo'd Hall. I have spent twenty thousand dollahs foh a single matron. How many hawses—truly great hawses —did such brood mayehs as that produce? How many do you think?"

Judge Dillon gave Mr. Sanford the warm look of a brother.

"Not many," he murmured.

"Well, I dunno, Mr. Sanford," said Blister. "You tells me about one—the filly that copped the Derby fur you."

"Yes; she was one. And one moh, suh. Two in all."

"I never hear you mention but the one," said Blister.

"The other never raced," explained Mr. Sanford. "I'll tell you why."

He lapsed into silence, into a sort of reverie, while we waited.

When he spoke it was totally without emotion. His voice was dull. It seemed somehow as though speech had been given to the dead past.

"It has been a long time," he said, more to himself than to us. "A long time!" he repeated, nodding thoughtfully, and again became silent.

"In those days," he began at last, "it was the custom of their mistress to go to the no'th pastuh with sugah, and call to the weanlin's. In flytime the youngstehs preferred the willow trees by the creek, and there was a qua'tah of a mile of level bluegrass from those willows to the pastuh gate. She would stand at the gate and call. As they heard her voice the colts would come oveh the creek bank as though it were a barrier—a fair start and no favohs asked. The rascals liked sugah, to be sure; but an excuse to fight it out foh a qua'tah was the main point of the game.

"One year a blood bay colt, black to the hocks and knees, was foaled in January. In June he got his sugah fuhst by two open lengths. In August he made them hang their heads foh shame—five, six, seven lengths he beat them; and their siahs watchin' from the paddocks.

"In the spring of his two-year-old fohm he suffered with an attack of distempah. He had been galloped on the fahm track by then, and we knew just what he was. We nuhsed him through it, and by the following spring he was ready to go out and meet them all foh the honoh of the pu'ple and white.

"Then, one night, I was wakened to be told that a doctah must be fetched and that each moment was precious. I sent my body sehvant to the bahns with the message that I wished a saddle on the best hawse in the stable. When pahtially dressed I followed him, and was thrown up by a stable man . . .

"There was a moon—a gracious moon, I remembah—the white road to Gawgetown, and a great fear at my heart. I did not know what was under me until I gave him his head on that white, straight road. Then I knew. I cannot say in what time we did those four miles; but this I can tell you—the colt ran the last mile as stanchly as the first, and one hour later he could barely walk. His terrific pace oveh that flinty road destroyed his tendons and broke the small bones in his legs. He gave his racin' life foh his lady, like the honest gentleman he was. His sacrifice, howeveh, was in vain . . . Death had the heels of him that night. Death had the heels of him!"

In a tense silence I seemed to hear a bell tolling. "Death had the heels of him!" it boomed over and over again.

Blister's eyes were starting from their sockets, but he did not hear the bell. He wet his parted lips.

"What become of him?" he breathed.

"When the place was sold he went with the rest. You have seen his descendants race on until his name has become a glory. The colt I rode that night was—Torch Bearer."

Blister drew in his breath with a whistling sound.

"Torch Bearer!" he gasped. "Did you own Torch Bearer?"

"I did, suh," came the quiet answer. "I bred and raised him. His blood flows in the veins of many—er—goats, I believe you call them."

"Man, oh, man!" said Blister, and became speechless.

I, too, was silent of necessity. There was something wrong with my throat.

And now Judge Dillon spoke, and it was apparent that he was afflicted like myself. Once more the big hand covered the thin knee.

"Mr. Sanford," I heard, "you can do me a favor if you will."

"My deah suh, name it!"

"Go to Lexington. Look over the colts at Thistle Ridge. If you find one good enough for the purple and white, bring him back here . . . He's yours."

I went along. Oh yes; I went along. I should miss two days of racing; but I would have missed more than that quite willingly. I was to see Old Man Sanford pick out one from a hundred colts— and all "bred clear to the clouds," as Blister explained to us on the train. I wondered whether any one of them would have that look— "the birthright of eagles"—and I hoped, I almost prayed, that we should find it.

That the colt was to be a purchase, not a gift, had made our journey possible. Five hundred dollars cash and "my note, suh, foh a like amount."

Judge Dillon had broken the deadlock by accepting; then offered his car for the trip to Lexington. At this a grin had appeared on Blister's face.

"No chance, Judge," he said.

"I thank you, suh, foh youh generosity," apologized Mr. Sanford. "It gives me the deepest pleasuh, the deepest gratification, suh; but, if you will pahdon me, I shall feel moh at home on the train."

"You couldn't get him in one of those things on a bet," Blister explained; and so a locomotive pulled us safely into Lexington.

We spent the night at the hotel and drove to Thistle Ridge early next morning behind a plodding pair. Even in Kentucky livery horses are—livery horses.

A letter from Judge Dillon opened the big gates wide and placed us in charge of one Wesley Washington. I reminded him of my previous visit to Thistle Ridge. He acknowledged it with no sign of enthusiasm.

"What kinda colt you want?" he asked Blister.

"A good one," answered Blister briefly.

Wesley sniffed.

"You ain' said nothin'," he stated. "Dat's all we got."

"You're lucky," Blister told him. "Well, trot 'em out."

Then Wesley waved his wand and they were trotted out; or, rather, they came rearing through the doorway of the biggest of the big stables. Bays, browns, blacks, sorrels, chestnuts, roans—they bubbled out at us in an endless stream. Attached precariously to each of them—this was especially true when they reared—was a Negro boy. These Wesley addressed in sparkling and figurative speech.

At last Blister shouted through the dust.

"Say," he said, "this ain't gettin' us nowhere. Holy fright! How many you got?"

"Dat ain't half," said Wesley ominously.

"Cut it out!" directed Blister. "You'll have me pop-eyed in a minute. We'll go through the stall 'n' pick out the live ones. This stuff's too young anyway. We want a two-year-old broke to the barrier. Have you got any?"

I turned to Mr. Sanford. He was standing hat in hand, as was his custom, his face ablaze.

"The grandest spectacle I have witnessed in thirty yeahs, suh!" he informed me.

"Has we got a two-yeah-old broke to de barrieh?" I heard from Wesley. "Hush! Jus' ambulate ovah disaway." He led us to a smaller stable. It contained two rows of box stalls with a wide alley down the middle. Through the iron gratings in each stall I could see a snakelike head. The door at the opposite end of the stable looked out on the tawny oval of the farm track, and suddenly something flashed across the doorway so quickly that I only guessed it to be a thoroughbred with a boy crouching along his neck.

Wesley's eye swept up and down the two lines of box stalls. He looked at Blister with a prideful gleam.

"All two-yeah-olds," he said, "an' ready to race."

If this statement made any impression it was concealed. Blister yawned and sauntered to the first stall on the right.

"Well, there might be a plater among 'em," he said. "This all you got?"

"Ain't dat enough?" inquired Wesley with a snort.

"Not if they're the culls," said Blister. "You read that letter, didn't you? We're to see 'em all. Don't forget that."

"Hyar dey is," said Wesley. "Jus' use yoh eyes an' yoh han's."

"All right," said Blister as he opened a stall door—"but don't hold nothin' out on us. Mr. Sanford here is an old friend of the Judge."

Wesley rolled an inspecting eye over Mr. Sanford.

"I ain't neveh seen him roun' hyar," he stated, and honors were easy.

The battle was on in earnest a moment later. The colt in the first stall was haltered and led out into the runway. He was jet black with a white star, and wonderful to see.

"Nothin' fineh on fo' laigs," said Wesley, and I mentally agreed with him; but Blister walked once round that glorious creature and waved him back into his stall.

"Yep," he said; "he's right good on four legs, but he'll be on three when that curb begins to talk to him."

"Shuh!" said Wesley in deep disgust. "You ain' goin' to call dat little fullness in de tendon a curb, is you? He'll die of ole aige an' neveh know he's got it."

"He dies of old age before I own him," said Blister, and walked to the second stall.

And so it went for an hour. Mr. Sanford was strangely silent. When he ventured an opinion at all it was to agree with Wesley, and I was disappointed. I had hoped for delightful dissertations, for superhuman judgments. I had expected to see a master at work with his chosen medium. Instead, he seemed a child in the hands of the skillful Wesley; and I felt that Blister was our only hope.

This opinion had become settled when the unexpected happened. After a more than careful inspection of a chestnut colt, Blister turned to Wesley.

"What's this colt done?" he asked.

"Half in fifty," Wesley stated. "Jus' play foh him."

"Put a boy on him 'n' let's see him move," said Blister.

Then Mr. Sanford spoke.

"It will be unnecessary," he said quietly. "I do not like him."

A puzzled expression spread itself over Blister's face.

"All right," he said with a shade of annoyance in his voice, "you're the doctor."

And then I noticed Wesley—Wesley, the adroit—and a look of amazement, almost of terror, was in his eyes as he stared at Mr. Sanford.

"Yessuh," he said with a gulp. "Yessuh." Then he pulled himself together. "Put him up, boy," he directed magnificently, and moved to the next stall.

I stayed behind and displayed a quarter cautiously.

"Do you like this colt?" I asked, looking the boy straight in the face.

For a moment he hesitated. Then:

"No, suh," he whispered.

"Why not?" I inquired.

There was a flicker of contempt in his eyes.

"He's a houn'," I barely heard as the quarter changed owners.

It was a well-spent quarter; it had purchased knowledge. I knew now that among our party was a pair of eyes that could look deep into the heart of things. Old they were and faded, those eyes; but I felt assured that a glistening flank could not deceive them.

We worked down one side of the stable and up the other. We had seen twenty colts when we arrived at the last stall. It contained a long-legged sorrel and Blister damned him with a grunt when he was lead out.

"If he ever gets tangled up," was his comment, "you don't get his legs untied that year. This all you got?"

Wesley assured him it was. We seemed to have reached an *impasse*. Then, as Blister frowned absently at the sorrel colt, a voice began singing just outside the stable. It was a rich treble and it chanted in a minor key. I saw the absent look wiped slowly from Blister's face. It was supplanted by a dawning alertness as he listened intently.

Suddenly he disappeared through the doorway and there came to me a regular scuff-scuff on the gravel outside, in time to the words of the song, which were these:

> *"Bay colt wuck in fo'ty-eight,*
> *Goin to de races—goin' to de races;*
> *Bay colt wuck in fo'ty-eight,*
> *Goin' to de races now."*

I felt my jaw begin to drop, for Blister's voice had joined the unknown singer's.

> *"Bay colt wuck in fo'ty-eight,*

sang the voice; and then a bellow from Blister:

> *"Goin to de races—goin' to de races."*

The voice repeated:

> *"Bay colt wuck in fo'ty-eight,"*

and resigned to Blister's:

"Goin' to de races now!"

I went hastily through that doorway and arrived at the following phenomena:

Exhibit A—One Negro boy, no more than three feet high. His shoes (I mention them first because they constituted one-half of the whole exhibit) were—But words are feeble—*prodigious, Gargantuan,* are only mildly suggestive of those shoes. His stockings —and now I cross my heart and hope to die—were pink and they were silk. Somewhere beneath their many folds two skinny legs performed the miracle of moving those unbelievable shoes through an intricate clog dance.

Exhibit B—One Blister Jones, patting with feet and hands an accompaniment to the wonders being performed by the marvelous shoes.

Both exhibits were entirely in earnest and completely absorbed. As has been already told, they were joined in song.

As I assured myself that the phenomena were real and not imaginary, the words of the song changed.

"Bay colt wuck in fo'ty-eight,"

came steadfastly from the smaller singer; but Blister, instead of "Going to the races," sang:

"Where's he at? Where's he at?"
"Bay colt wuck in fo'ty-eight,"

insisted Exhibit A; and Exhibit B sang:

"Where's that bay colt now?"

They learn early, in Kentucky, that track and farm secrets are sacred. A suspicion of all outsiders, though dulled by the excitement of other folks' appreciation, still flickered somewhere in the dome of Exhibit A. The song was twice repeated without variation, and the "Where's he at?" became tragic in it's pleading tone.

At last Exhibit A must have decided that his partner in song was a kindred spirit and worthy of trust. At any rate,

"Oveh in de coolin' shed—oveh in de coolin' shed," I heard; and Blister brought the duet to a triumphant close with:
"Oveh in the coolin' shed now!"

He swung round and grinned at Wesley, who was standing stupefied in the doorway.

"Why, Wes!" he said reproachfully. "I'm surprised at you!"

Wesley glowered at Exhibit A.

"You ramble!" he said and the marvelous shoes bore their owner swiftly from our sight.

So, through song, was the wily Wesley brought to confusion. We found four two-year-olds in the long, squatty cooling shed, and Wesley admitted, under pressure, that they were the pick of their year, kept for special training.

Three of them stood in straw to their knees, confined in three tremendous box stalls. One was being led under blankets up and down the runway. His sides lifted their covering regularly. His clean-cut velvet nostrils widened and contracted as he took his breath. His eyes were blazing jewels. To him went Blister, like iron filings to a magnet.

"Peel him fur a minute," he said, and the still dazed and somewhat chastened Wesley nodded his permission.

Then appeared the most perfect living creature I had ever seen. He was a rich bay—now dark mahogany because of a recent bath—and the sheer beauty of him produced in me a feeling of awe, almost of worship. I was moved as though I listened to the Seventh Symphony or viewed the Winged Victory; and this was fit and proper, for my eyes were drinking in a piece by the greatest of all masters.

Blister was cursing softly, reverently, as though he were at prayer.

"If he's only half as good as he looks!" he sighed at last. "How about *him,* Mr. Sanford?"

I had forgotten Old Man Sanford. I now discovered him standing before a stall and gazing raptly at what was within. At Blister's words he turned and surveyed the bay colt.

"The most superb piece of hawseflesh," he said," I have eveh had the pleasuh of observing. I could not fault him with a microscope. He is nothing shawt of perfection, suh—nothing shawt of perfection." His eyes lingered for an instant on the wet flanks of the uncovered colt. "He's too wahm to be without his clothing," he suggested, and turned again to the stall before him.

Blister covered the colt with one dexterous swing. He glanced at the name embroidered on the blankets.

"Postman," he read aloud. "He'll be by Messenger, won't he?" The boy at the colt's head nodded. "Worked in forty-eight just now, eh?" said Blister to no one in particular. Again the boy nodded. "Well," decided Blister, "we'll take a chance on him. Train fur Looeyville at four o'clock—ain't they, Wes?"

Wesley gave a moan of anguish.

"My Gawd!" he said.

"What's bitin' you?" demanded Blister. "We're payin' for him, ain't we?"

"Lemme have dat letter one moh time," said Wesley. He absorbed the letter's contents as though it were poison, and came at last to the fatal "John C. Dillon" at the end. This he read aloud and slowly shook his head. "He's los' his min'," he stated, and glared at Mr. Sanford. "What you payin' fo' dis hyar colt?" he demanded.

Mr. Sanford glanced in our direction. His eyes had a far-away look.

"Were you addressing me?" he asked.

"Yessuh," replied Wesley. "I was inquirin' de price you aim to pay foh dis colt."

"That is a matteh," said Old Man Sanford, "that concerns only yoh employeh and myself. Howeveh, I am not going to pu'chase the colt to which you refeh." He glanced dreamily into the stall before which he seemed rooted. "I have taken a fancy to my little friend in hyah. . . . Could you oblige me with a piece of sugah?"

As one man, Blister and I made a rush for that stall. We peered through the bars for a moment and our amazed eyes met. In Blister's an angry despair was dawning. He turned savagely on Mr. Sanford.

"You goin' to buy that shrimp?" he demanded.

"Yes, suh," said Old Man Sanford mildly. "I expect to pu'chase him. . . . Ah, heah's the sugah!" He took some lumps of sugar from the now beaming Wesley and opened the stall door.

Blister stepped inside the stall and devoted some moments to vain pleadings. Mr. Sanford was unmoved by them.

Then the storm broke. Blister became a madman who raved. He cursed not only the small black two-year-old, standing knee-deep in golden straw, but the small, white-haired old gentleman who was placidly feeding him sugar. The storm raged on, but Mr. Sanford gave no sign.

At last I saw a hand that was extended to the colt's muzzle begin to tremble, and I took Blister by the arm and drew him forcefully away.

"Stop!" I said in an undertone. "You're doing no good and he's an old man."

Blister tore his arm from mine.

"He's an old fool!" he cried. "He's chucking away the chance of a lifetime!" Then his eye fell on the bay colt and his voice became a wail. "Ain't it hell?" he inquired of high heaven. "Ain't it just hell?"

At this point Wesley saw fit to emit a loud guffaw. Blister advanced on him like a tiger.

"Laugh, you boob!" he shot out, and Wesley's joyous expression vanished.

I saw that I was doing no good and joined Mr. Sanford in the stall.

"Rather small, isn't he?" I suggested.

"He could be a little larger," Mr. Sanford admitted. "He could stand half a han' and fifty pounds moh at his aige; but then, he'll grow. He'll make a hawse some day."

And now came Blister, rather sheepish, and stood beside us.

"I got sore, Mr. Sanford," he said. "I oughta be kicked!"

Old Man Sanford proffered a lump of sugar to the slim black muzzle. It was accepted so eagerly that the sugar was knocked from the extended hand. Mr. Sanford pointed a reproving finger at the colt.

"Not quite so fast, young man!" he admonished. Then he turned to Blister with a gentle smile. "Youth is hasty," he said, "and sometimes—mistaken."

I returned to Cincinnati and work that night, filled with speculations about a small black colt and his new owner. The latter, I felt, had reached a stubborn dotage.

Two months rolled by; they crawled for me. . . . The powers above decreed that the paper should fight the Bull Moose to the death. I trained the guns of the editorial page on a dauntless smile and adored its dynamic owner in secret.

Those were full days, but I found time somehow for a daily glance at the racing news. One morning I read the following:

> Postman, a bay colt, bred and owned by John C. Dillon, captured the two-year-old event without apparent effort. It was the winner's first appearance under colors. He is a big, rangy youngster, handsome as a picture. He appears to be a very high-class colt and should be heard from.

"Poor Blister," I thought; and later, as I read again and again of smashing victories by a great and still greater Postman, I became quite venomous when I thought of Old Man Sanford. I referred to him mentally as "That old fool!" and imagined Blister in horrid depths of despair.

Then the bugle called for the last time that year at Lexington, and the thoroughbreds came to my very door to listen for it.

For days thereafter, as luck would have it, I was forced to pound my typewriter viciously, everlastingly, and was too tired when night came to do more than stagger to bed. At last there came a lull and I fled incontinently to Latonia and the world of horse.

I approached Blister's stalls as one draws near a sepulcher. I felt that my voice, when I addressed him, should be pitched as though in the presence of a casket. I was shocked, therefore, at his lightness of mien.

"Hello, Four Eyes!" he said cheerfully. "How's the ole scout?"

I assured him that my scouting days were not yet over. And then: "I've been reading about Postman," I said.

"Some colt!" said Blister. "He's bowed 'em home five times now. They've made him favorite fur the Hammond against all them Eastern babies."

There was genuine enthusiasm in his voice and I was filled with admiration for a spirit that could take a blow so jauntily. His attitude was undoubtedly the correct one, but I could not accomplish it. I thought of the five thousand dollars that went, with the floral horseshoe, to the winner of the Hammond Stakes. I thought of a gentle, fine, threadbare old man who needed that five thousand —Oh, so desperately—and I was filled with bitter regret, with malice and bad words.

"Of course he'll win it!" I burst out spitefully.

"Why, I dunno," drawled Blister, and added, "I thought Judge Dillon was a friend of yours."

"Oh, damn!" I said.

"Why, Four Eyes!" said Blister. " 'N' Chick listenin' to you too!"

Chick grinned appreciatively. "Don't let him kid ya," he advised. "He wasn't so gay hisself till—"

"Take a shot of grape juice," interrupted Blister, " 'n' hire a hall."

Chick's voice trailed off into unintelligible mutterings as he turned away.

"How about Mr. Sanford's colt?" I asked. "Have you still got him?"

To my astonishment Blister broke into one of his rare fits of laughter. He all but doubled up with unaccountable mirth.

"Say, Chick," he called when he could control his voice, "he wants to know if we still got the Sanford colt!"

Chick had turned a rather glum face our way; but at the words his expression became instantly joyous.

"Oh, say!" he said.

Then began a series of hilarious exchanges, entirely without meaning to me.

"He's hangin' around somewhere, ain't he, Chick?"

"The black colt."

"Why, maybe he is," said Chick.

"You still throw a little rough feed into him occasionally, don't you, Chick?"

"When I got the time," said Chick; and the two imbeciles roared with laughter.

At last Blister began beating me between the shoulder blades.

"We got him, Four Eyes," he told me between thumps. "Yep—we got him."

"Stop!" I shouted. "What the devil's the matter with you?"

Blister became serious.

"Come here!" he said, and dragged me to a stall. He threw back the upper door and a shaft of sunlight streamed into the stall's interior, bathing a slim black head and neck until they glistened like a vein of coal. "Know him?" asked Blister.

"Yes," I said. "He's bigger though."

"Look at him good!" ordered Blister.

I peered at the relaxed inmate of the stall, who blinked sleepily at me through the shaft of sunlight. Blister pulled me back, closed the stall door, and tightened his grip on my arm.

"Now listen!" he said. "You just looked at the best two-year-old God ever put breath in."

I took in this incredible information slowly. I exulted in it for a moment, and then came doubts.

"How do you know?" I demanded.

"How do I know!" exclaimed Blister. "It 'ud take me a week to tell you. Man, he can fly! He makes his first start tomorrow—in the Hammond. Old Man Sanford'll get in tonight. Come out'n see a real colt run."

My brain was whirling.

"In the Hammond?" I gasped. "Does Mr. Sanford know all this?"

Blister gave me a slow, a thoughtful look.

"It sounds nutty," he said; "but I can't figger it no other way. As sure as you 'n' me are standin' here—he knowed it from the very first!"

Until I closed my eyes that night I wondered whether Blister's words were true. If so, what sort of judgment, instinct, intuition had been used that day at Thistle Ridge? I gave it up at last and slept, to dream of a colt that suddenly grew raven wings and soared over the grandstand while I nodded wisely and said: "Of course—the birthright of eagles!"

I got to Blister's stalls at one o'clock next day, and found Mr. Sanford clothed in a new dignity hard to describe. Perhaps he had donned it with the remarkable flowered waistcoat he wore—or was it due to his flowing double-breasted coat, a sprightly blue in color and suggesting inevitably a leather trunk, dusty, attic-bound, which had yawned and spat it forth?

"Welcome, suh; thrice welcome!" he said to me. "I take the liberty of presuming that the pu'ple and white is honored with yoh best wishes today."

I assured him from the bottom of my heart that this was so. He wrung my hand again and took out a gold watch the size of a bun.

"Three hours moh," he said, "before our hopes are realized or shattered."

"You think the colt will win?" I inquired.

Mr. Sanford turned to the southwest. I followed his eyes and saw a bank of evil-looking clouds creeping slowly up the sky.

"I like our chances, suh," he told me; "but it will depend on those clouds yondeh. We want a fast track foh the little chap. He is a swallow. Mud would break his heart."

"She's fast enough now," said Blister, who had joined us; and Mr. Sanford nodded.

So for three hours I watched the sky prayerfully and saw it become more and more ominous. When the bugle called for the Hammond at last, Latonia was shut off from the rest of the world by an inverted inky cup, its sides shot now and then with lightning flashes. We seemed to be in a great vacuum. I found my lungs snatching for each breath, while my racing card grew limp as I clutched it spasmodically in a sweating hand.

I had seen fit to take a vital interest in the next few moments; but

I glanced at faces all about me in the grandstand and found them strained and unnatural. Perhaps in the gloom they seemed whiter than they really were; perhaps my own nerves pricked my imagination until this packed humanity became one beating heart.

I do not think that this was so. The dramatic moment goes straight to the soul of a crowd, and this crowd was to see the Hammond staged in a breathless dark, with the lightning's flicker for an uncertain spotlight.

No rain would spoil our chances that day, for now, across the center field at the half-mile post, a mass of colors boiled at the barrier. The purple and white was somewhere in the shifting, surging line, borne by a swallow, so I had been told. Well, even so, the blue and gold was there likewise—and carried by what? Perhaps an eagle!

Suddenly a sigh—not the customary roar, but a deep intaking of the grandstand's breath—told me they were on the wing. I strained my eyes at the blurred mass of them, which seemed to move slowly in the distance as it reached the far turn of the back stretch. Then a flash of lightning came and my heart skipped a beat and sank.

They were divided into two unequal parts. One was a crowded, indistinguishable mass. The other, far ahead in unassailable isolation, was a single spot of bay with a splash of color clinging above.

A roar of "Postman!" shattered the quiet like a bombshell, for that splash of color was blue and gold. The favorite was making a runaway race of it. He was coming home to twenty thousand joyful backers, who screamed and screamed his name.

Until that moment I had been the victim of a dream. I had come to believe that the little old man, standing silent at my side, possessed an insight more than human. Now I had wakened. He was an old fool in a preposterous coat and waistcoat, and I looked at him and laughed a mirthless laugh. He was squinting slightly as he peered with his washed-out eyes into the distance. His face was placid; and as I noticed this I told myself that he was positively witless. Then he spoke.

"The bay colt is better than I thought," he said.

"True," I agreed bitterly and noted, as the lightning flashed again, that the blue and gold was an amazing distance ahead of those struggling mediocre others.

"A pretty race," murmured Old Man Sanford; and now I thought him more than doddering—he was insane.

Some seconds passed in darkness, while the grandstand gave off a contented murmur. Then suddenly the murmur rose to a new note. It held fear and consternation in it. My eyes leaped up the track. The bay colt had rounded the curve into the stretch. He was coming down the straight like a bullet; but—miracle of miracles!—it was plain that he was not alone. . . . .

In a flash it came to me: stride for stride, on the far side of him, one other had maintained a flight equal to his own. And then I went mad; for this other, unsuspected in the darkness until now, commenced to creep slowly, surely, into the lead. Above his stretching neck his colors nestled proudly. He was bringing the purple and white safe home to gold and glory.

Nearer and nearer he came, this small demon whose coat matched the heavens, and so shot past us, with the great Postman— under the whip—two lengths behind him!

I remember executing a sort of bear dance, with Mr. Sanford enfolded in my embrace. I desisted when a smothered voice informed me that my conduct was "unseemly, suh—most unseemly!"

A rush to the track followed, where we found Blister, quite pale, waiting with a blanket. Suddenly the grandstand, which had groaned once and become silent, broke into a roar that grew and grew.

"What is it?" I asked.

Blister whirled and stared at the figures on the timing board. I saw a look of awe come into his face.

"What is it?" I repeated. "Why are they cheering? Is it the time?"

"Oh, no!" said Blister with scornful sarcasm and a look of pity at my ignorance. "It ain't the time!" He nodded at the figures. "That's only the world's record fur the age 'n' distance."

And now there came, mincing back to us on slender, nervous

"The look of eagles."

legs, something wet and black and wonderful. It pawed and danced wildly in a growing ring of curious eyes.

Then, just above the grandstand, the inky cup of the sky was broken and there appeared the light of an unseen sun. It turned the piled white clouds in the break to marvels of rose and gold. They seemed like the ramparts of heaven, set there to guard from earthly eyes the abode of the immortals.

"Whoa, man! Whoa, hon!" said Blister, and covered the heaving sides.

As he heard Blister's voice and felt the touch of the blanket the colt grew quiet. His eyes became less fiery wild. He raised his head, with its dilated blood-red nostrils, and stared—not at the mortals standing reverently around him, but far beyond our gaze—through the lurid gap in the sky, straight into Valhalla.

I felt a hand on my arm.

"The look of eagles, suh!" said Old Man Sanford.

The Straight Goer

Will H. Ogilvie

The ringing, hanging hen-roost thief—we have no use for him;
When they tear him up and eat him not a single eye grows dim;
But when a straight-necked traveller goes gallantly away
We grieve not if we lose him, for he'll run another day.

The loafing, skirting, loud-mouthed hound that hangs about your horse
The while his bolder comrades gather thorn-wounds in the gorse—

We care not if he stops a kick or ties himself in wire,
The leader running straight and true's the hound of our desire.

Give me the fox that holds his point though fools and fate combine,
Give me the hounds that follow him with nose upon the line,
The horse that never turns his head at fence or five-barred gate,
The man who has the needful nerve to cross a country straight!

And in the larger field of life let skirters stand aside,
Make way for those who want to work and those who dare to ride!
The only one who's worth a place to risk a fall with fate
Is he who steels his gallant heart and rides his country straight.

Putnam — U.S. Army

If you look through old army records, you will find the facts of this story confirmed. This unpretentious and straightforward account of the most famous horse of the United States Army was prepared for me by an army officer.

This famous war horse of Reilly's Light Battery F, 5th Field Artillery, entered the service of the United States with a group of other horses purchased by the government in San Francisco. He was issued to the Yale Light Battery of Niantic, Connecticut in 1898 and served with this battery during the Spanish-American War.

On the muster out of the Yale Battery, he was transferred to the quartermaster at Fort Hamilton, New York, where he was assigned to Reilly's Light Battery F, then stationed at that fort. Here he was given the name of Putnam in memory of the famous General Israel Putnam of Revolutionary War fame. The horse entered into the work of the battery and consistently lived up to his great name, as his subsequent record proved.

Since no pictures of the famous horse are extant, the following description furnished by Major General Summerall, formerly a lieutenant in Reilly's Battery, will give an idea of this magnificent horse:

"Putnam, or Peking, as he was afterwards called, was a large, handsome animal of a dark bay color and with many points that indicated fine breeding, probably bred from Percheron and thoroughbred stock. He weighed about 1,600 pounds and was 16 or 16½ hands high. He had a very broad forehead, prominent eyes, fine small ears, a delicate muzzle, large nostrils, rather fine lips and a large throat and chest. He was so perfectly proportioned that he would have attracted attention in any group of horses. His mane was rather short and bushy and remained that way, and his tail reached about to the hocks."

Because of his intelligence and responsiveness, as well as his attractive appearance, the horse at once became a great favorite in the battery. He was assigned as near wheel horse of the first piece, which is really the post of honor in the team. The battery was never able to secure an appropriate mate, because any other horse, no matter how well proportioned, suffered at once by comparison.

At the beginning of the insurrection in April 1899, Battery F was ordered to the Philippines. They were allowed to take only twenty-four horses, and naturally Putnam was one of the first chosen to go. The journey to the islands was uneventful, but when the battery took to the field it was found that the two horses and the two mules supplied for each carriage were seldom able to negotiate the boggy rice paddies and the difficult ground encountered in the rough country. But "Old Put," as he was affectionately called, always brought his gun into place promptly and there was never any cause for worry as to what he would do.

Putnam participated in the campaigns in the Philippines for more than a year and materially assisted in the victories by his promptness in getting his gun into the assigned position.

The Boxer Uprising in China in 1900 necessitated an expedition there, and Reilly's Battery F, 5th Field Artillery was incorporated into the forces sent, sailing from Manila the middle of July.

For twenty-one days the horses were kept in their narrow stalls on shipboard, and during that time the seas were so rough that it was almost impossible for the horses to keep their footing. Seasick and suffering, the animals endured untold agony, which the soldiers did their best to alleviate. They spent much of their time with them attending to their wants, and attempting to assuage their fright. During this trying time the intelligence of Putnam was the subject of much comment, and great affection was expressed for the re-markable horse.

The battery eventually arrived in China and while marching along a sunken road, a characteristic of the country, the order came to occupy a position immediately on the high ground near the road. The cut was so deep that the banks rose above the heads of the mounted men. The command was given to move the battery up the road embankment, and the leaders of the first piece, which was in front, were turned without hesitation and scrambled up the bank. The swing followed in a similar manner, and then the wheel horses with the driver mounted on Putnam, followed by the heavy gun. But no sooner had the wheels touched the foot of the embankment than the trace spring of the off-wheel horse snapped and the entire team, with the exception of Putnam, ceased their efforts.

In describing the incident, the officers of the battery say they never saw anything like it before. Putnam, manifestly conscious of the duty that rested upon him and of the crisis that must be met, settled himself unhesitatingly, and slowly and continuously crawled up the steep, slippery cliff, pulling the heavy gun and its carriage after him, doing the work of three horses. He required no urging and the whole thing happened so quickly that nothing could be done to assist him.

When the gun was on open ground the team continued their advance, and there before the eyes of the American forces were the tall walls of Peking surmounted with pagodas and fortifications from which poured a continuous, murderous fire upon the advancing troops.

The din was terrific, but unmindful of it, Putnam brought his gun into position. It was quickly unlimbered and opened fire, getting the range almost immediately, and reducing the great pagoda filled with Chinese troops at the southeast angle of the wall. The other guns followed but the crisis had passed. For with one gun in action and firing rapidly, the infantry received the support it needed, and advanced under their own fire to attack the great gate guarding the entrance to the Chinese city. A few well directed shells from the American guns pierced the heavy iron-bound planks and the Boxers, seeing their supposedly impregnable gate giving way, retreated in haste. So into the ancient city of Peking, the American troops poured, pursuing the fleeing Boxers up the long avenue, while Putnam and the other horses brought the great guns forward as they were needed.

The battery had many casualties, the most serious being the loss of its gallant commander, Captain Reilly, who was killed on the Water Gate the morning of August 15. Putnam escaped injury and was praised by all who saw him for his gallant action and unflinching service during the terrific fighting. For two days the exhausted men and horses neither stopped to eat or sleep, and they were well deserving of the attentions bestowed upon them by the grateful legations.

When Reilly's Battery was relieved, the horses were transferred to McComb's Battery. The story of "Old Put" went with him and his new masters became as devoted as his old ones. There was great rivalry in McComb's Battery to secure "Old Put" for the different teams, each one feeling honored to have such a hero in his team.

In honor of his gallant services in China, "Old Put" was re-christened Peking, and ever afterwards called by that name. When Peking became enfeebled with age, he was relieved of all work and given every attention that human affection could devise. A general order of the Philippines department officials retired him, and forage was authorized for him until his death.

The order recites the achievements of Peking which merited his official retirement, and contains nineteen endorsements signed by the officers of various departments through which the order passed. The first endorsement is signed by Brigadier General John J. Pershing, then in command at Fort William McKinley:

> Headquarters
> Fort William McKinley
> June 21, 1908

> This horse (Putnam) deserves consideration that should be shown for faithful service, and has earned the right to live to the end of his natural life at the expense of the government.

> *John J. Pershing*
> *Brigadier General, U.S.A.*

Peking died in his twentieth year, and authority was obtained to bury him on a hill outside Fort William McKinley. A grave was dug and here was placed the mortal remains of the most famous horse of the United States Army. Behind the caisson which held the flag-draped body, the members of the battery and the many friends of the noted horse followed to the solemn tones of the funeral dirge played by the band. A firing squad paid a last tribute to Peking, as befitted a hero and a veteran, and then a bugler sounded *Taps* for "Old Put."

Major General Summerall, a lieutenant in Battery F at the time Peking performed his memorable feat, and an eyewitness to his gallant action which won him his retirement by the War Department, paid the following tribute to his memory:

"The example of this horse was a great factor in the morale of a battery that itself was an ornament to our service. The men who knew him will never cease to take pride in telling of his courage, his loyalty, and his ability. In his way, he exemplified the highest fulfillment of living and duty."

Pawnee

C. W. Anderson

Louis Alberginni was for many years the beloved huntsman with Groton Hunt. He knew horses and hounds as few men do. This story is mostly fiction, but the character of Louis is true to life. It all could have happened. (–From A Filly for Joan)

Many people like riding but only a few get all the pleasure that there is in riding a fine horse. You have to love horses, and you must also try to perfect your riding. So many are satisfied if they can just stick on a horse. That's like being satisfied with playing the piano with one finger. To be a fine rider you must understand horses thoroughly. You must understand what they think. An experienced horseman knows just what a horse will do, what will frighten him or make him nervous. An unexpected shy can throw an unsuspecting rider; many get hurt that way. I once knew a horse that was such a terrific shier that his owner finally gave him away. And he'd paid fifteen hundred dollars for him!"

"Couldn't he be cured at all, Louis?"

"Well I can't quite say I cured him. I helped him some and he helped me a lot. After I had him I never rode slack or careless on any horse. He could really shy. He'd drop from under you, and you'd think he was falling; but he just spread his legs wide, and then he'd go about six feet to the side in a leap that was like lightning. If you weren't riding a close seat with a good knee grip you were gone. He'd thrown his owner and everyone else that tried to ride him so often that they finally gave up and no one wanted him.

"If he hadn't been such a grand-looking horse I wouldn't have taken him, even as a gift. What could I do with him? I couldn't put

"It was a quick, knowing eye with a glint in it. And the ears were very alert and always moving."

anyone I was teaching on him and I couldn't use him myself, for teaching. A shy could unsettle a quiet horse.

"And you could just imagine my trying to hunt hounds with him. I had plenty of horses to feed already, but there was something about him that got me. He was proud and high-headed with a wonderful sloping shoulder. It was a pleasure just to look at him. I've had a lot of horses in my day but do you know I still remember that wonderful top line of his. It flowed from his ear over a beautifully set wither, through a short back, with just enough room for a saddle. His quarters were perfect. I thought even if I couldn't do anything with him just to have a horse like that around to look at everyday would make you feel good. He was everything a horseman dreams of except maybe the eye. It was a quick, knowing eye with a glint in it. And the ears were very alert and always moving. I said to myself, 'This horse sees too much.' "

"What do you mean, Louis? I thought it was good for a horse to have keen eyes."

"A horse can be a shier because his eyesight is poor; he doesn't see things until they are on top of him. But if a horse has too quick an eye, he's apt to be startled because he gets a quick glimpse of something far away. He never gets the whole story until it's too late. A big powerful horse would not be apt to be afraid of a bird or a squirrel or rabbit if he saw it full and clear, but when he sees a flash of something moving suddenly, it's different. And this fellow, Pawnee, had another angle that helped explain everything. He'd been raised in the west—Wyoming I think it was. That didn't mean anything to me at first except to be surprised he'd been broken gentle instead of cowboy fashion. The first time I sat on him I could tell no spur had ever touched this horse. It would be like trying to put out a fire with gasoline."

"What did his being raised in the west have to do with his shying, Louis?"

"Well, I was riding him one day, along a hard road and a dried leaf blew across the road making a rattling sound. Pawnee dropped and gave a sideways leap that took us clear into the ditch. I found myself halfway up his neck. If he had given another jump I would have been off, but he let me get back into the saddle and find my stirrups. I'd ridden many horses that shied but nothing like that. It was chained lightning. But I realized it wasn't a trick—all he would have had to do was to give an extra buck and he would have gotten rid of me if that's what he wanted. No, he was really frightened. And suddenly I knew why.

"Heels out a little more," said Louis looking over at Joan. "Don't grip with the lower part of your leg. Keep the grip in the thigh and the knee."

"I'm sorry, Louis. I'll remember. Why did a dry leaf frighten him so?"

"I kept thinking about it. That was the most terrific shy he ever showed me and I knew he was frightened. Then it came to me. I spent a summer out west when I was a youngster, and one day after I came back I remember jumping almost out of my skin at the sound of a dry leaf blowing over the sidewalk. It was exactly the sound that a rattlesnake makes when he is about to strike! And a horse is deathly afraid of snakes. He'd probably seen plenty of them and when he heard that rattle he was taking no chances. Then I began to get the whole picture. Out west everything was in the open and clear to see. Outside of snakes almost anything that moved would be seen a long distance away. Nothing appeared suddenly and unexpectedly. Then he was brought back here where the country is all enclosed. His eyes had been trained by those long distances to notice things as sharply as a western pony or an Indian. Here he saw too much, too suddenly. He hadn't gotten used to it—probably never would. At least that's the way it looked to me."

"What did you do with him then? I know you tried to cure him but how did you go about it?"

"He'd go around with his head in the air, his nostrils flaring, carrying his tail like a flag."

"First I put him in a box stall that had windows on two sides and I cleaned those windows thoroughly. One looked out on a road where quite a bit of traffic went by. I wanted him to see everything. I'd found out that the stall he'd had was dark; no window, and there was no paddock. And he was as tight as a violin string; you could feel it when you got into the saddle; think what that must have done to him. It wouldn't be good for any horse. But for him, raised as he was, it was much worse."

"The poor horse!" exclaimed Joan. "He must have been happy in that new stall."

"He was and you should have seen him in that big paddock. He'd go around with his head in the air, his nostrils flaring, carrying his tail like a flag. He was really something to see."

"How was he for riding? Was he better about shying?" asked Joan.

"He improved but when something startled him, he still put in a terrific one. It would have put most riders down. I tried to keep my eyes open to see things as quickly as he did so I'd be ready for his shy, but that was hard to do. He had the eye of a hawk, and when he let go, it was like a steel spring uncoiled. But you couldn't get mad at him. He couldn't help it."

Louis paused a moment. "He did something once that I'd never seen before and never expect to see again. We were riding along this road, and a partridge went up just in front of us. You know how they can explode and really startle you. Pawnee almost came apart. His shy was so violent that he went to his knees when he landed. Anytime a horse goes to his knees you can be pretty sure he's going down. But not that horse. He went along on his knees for a half a dozen strides and came up again! I don't know how he did it. It must have been his pride. He was the proudest horse I've ever known. I don't believe he'd ever been down, and he wasn't going to begin then."

"You must have loved that horse, Louis. Whatever became of him?"

"Well, I couldn't put anybody on him; it was too risky. I'd get up an hour early just to get him out. Lord knows I had plenty of horses that had to be exercised, but there was something about this horse that made riding seem all new again. He was really a person. There was a young boy who had begun riding at the stable. He hadn't had much training, but he was mad about horses and learned quickly. I noticed when he paid me for his ride some of the money would be quarters and dimes. I knew the way he felt about horses, he would be riding much oftener if he could afford it. So I offered him the chance to exercise some of the horses. You should have seen his face light up."

"Oh Louis, that was a nice thing to do."

"It worked out well for me, too. He was a natural with horses. He learned more in two months than many riders do in two years. But one thing I noticed; he couldn't stay away from Pawnee. He liked all the horses, but he always lingered longest at Pawnee's stall. And the horse seemed to like him. I knew he was dying to ride the horse but I wasn't sure how it would work out. Finally one day I told him he could take Pawnee out. I still remember the look on his face. I don't know if he even heard me when I warned him about his shying. He just stood looking at the horse as if it were Man o' War himself.

"They were gone a long time, and I'd begun to worry when I saw them coming down the road. The boy had Pawnee on a loose rein and the horse was trotting as gaily as I'd ever seen him. I didn't need to ask how they'd gotten along. The way the horse rubbed his head against the boy's shoulder told the story. When I saw that he had brought the horse in nice and quiet and not a wet hair on him, I said he could ride Pawnee whenever he wanted to. Often he was over at daybreak to get a ride before school or work that had to be done. The more I saw of them the more I realized that boy and horse belonged together. I kept turning things over in my mind, and one day I drove over to his place. They had a small farm near Lynford, well kept, mostly garden stuff. I found the boy out at the stable. He was just finishing a box stall. It was made of old lumber but it was a fine job. Everything was there, feed box, rack for water bucket, bracket for salt block and two good windows.

" 'I didn't know you were getting a horse,' I said.

"He looked a little flustered. 'Maybe some day,' he said. 'But I had to have a stable first. Now I'll start to save up for a horse.' "

"Oh, I hope he got his horse," cried Joan.

"He did," said Louis. "I rode over before dawn leading Pawnee and put him in the stall without anyone seeing me. I'd liked to have seen that boy's face when he came down to the stable."

Joan looked at Louis earnestly. "Oh, Louis," she said, "you are such a nice man."

The Ride of His Life

David Gray

David Gray's stories, written at the turn of the century, dealt with that time when the horse was an important adjunct to life. Cars were rare, tractors unknown, and the horse was indispensable. Every man was, of necessity, a horseman; at least enough of a horseman to tack up a horse for riding or driving. But for many, the love of fine horseflesh was compelling, and much of their spare time was spent with horses. Such a one was the author of this story, for firsthand knowledge of horses runs through all his stories.

Cordillas Y Sandoval was an attaché of the Spanish legation, whom Varick invited to Oakdale to please Mrs. Varick and, more especially, her widowed sister.

"I believe I met him once at the club in Washington," Varick remarked.

"I thought he was rather an ass; but we've plenty of stable-room. Does he hunt?"

Mrs. Innis, the sister-in-law, was afraid he did,—in a hunting-country men who do not ride are at a premium,—but was uncertain about it; therefore upon his arrival the question was referred to Cordillas himself.

The Spaniard dashed Mrs. Innis's hopes. He asserted that he was "practised in equestrianism," and "worshiped horses."

"Yes, and I haf yoomp, too," he added. Then he branched off on the merits of his "fiery-eyed steed" in Madrid, which he was bound to believe would make an unparalleled "yoomper," although, as there was no fox-hunting in his country, its ability had never been called out.

"I can see," said Varick, pleasantly interrupting, "that you are the man for us. I shall put you up on that good horse Thomas Dooley." There was duplicity in this, for Varick distrusted the horsemanship of all Latin foreigners; but the Spaniard suspected it not, and the sister-in-law discreetly held her peace.

Thomas Dooley, at the time when fate introduced him to Cordillas, was going on seventeen, and he knew more about getting across a hunting-country than men usually acquire in half a century. His ancestry was not discussed, but he had the best box-stall in Varick's stable, and would be gloriously pensioned when his time of service expired. Ten years back he had exchanged the plow for the saddle, as the result of a memorable humiliation which he put upon the entire Oakdale Hunt. One dismal, sloppy morning Dooley had appeared at a meet, ridden by a farmer's boy. Not long after the hounds had found, twenty angry men were sitting on as many sulky, discouraged horses in a deep-plowed field waiting for some-one to break the fence in front of them. They were not soothed when they saw Dooley playfully switch his flowing tail over five feet of new oak rails, and disappear after the pack. Varick had been one of these men; and that same afternoon he possessed Thomas Dooley, who ever since had carried him with unerring judgment and ability. As the years went by, Dooley came to be known as Varick's "morning-after" horse, and he never betrayed the confidence this title implied. Nevertheless, it must be said that, for a man whose nerves had not been outraged, Dooley could hardly be called an agreeable mount.

He was, by general admission, the plainest horse that ever followed hounds. His legs and feet were coarse, and he galloped with as much spring as if he were on stilts. The mighty quarters wherein dwelt his genius for getting over high timber were so much too big for him that he seemed to have got another horse's hind legs by mistake. He had a mouth no bit could conquer. He chose what he would jump, and how, regardless of his rider. Only the certainty that he would never fall made him venerated, and most persons who hunt resent the imputation that they need this kind of horse. If a man's heart is strong with sleep and November air, there is little satisfaction in being carried over the country by a machine.

When Cordillas made his first appearance on Thomas Dooley, it was noted that he rode with uncommonly long stirrup-leathers,—too long for hunting,—and sat as stiff as a horse-guard, bouncing dismally with Thomas's hard trot. The tails of his pink coat were unsullied by the loin-sweat of the chase, and there was no mark of stirrup-iron across the instep of his freshly treed boots.

" 'E's quite noo," remarked the first whip, in an undertone.

"With Thomas," replied the huntsman, " 'e won't be long noo."

"Dooley bucking over from good ground, his rider with him, although well toward his ears."

The hounds found unexpectedly, and the advice Varick intended to give his guest was cut short.

"Don't try to steer him at his fences," he yelled; "it won't do any good." The next moment the rattle-headed four-year-old he was riding took off in a bit of marsh, and became mixed up with a panel of boards. Varick got up in time to see Dooley bucking over from good ground, his rider with him, although well on toward his ears.

"I guess he'll do; he's got to," said Varick, softly swearing at his muddied boots. He scrambled up into the saddle, saw his guest slide back into his, and together they swept on after the hounds.

For the most part, Cordillas managed to remain inconspicuous, though he took a spectacular "voluntary" on the way back to the kennels. He tried to "lark" Dooley over a wayside fence, possibly for the benefit of Mrs. Innis, who was driving by in her cart. Dooley, knowing that the jump was needless, stopped at the fence and the Spaniard went over alone; but his heart seemed to be in the right place, and he got up again, laughing.

The next time he went out, on a hint from Varick he shortened his leathers, thrust his feet home through the irons, and really did very creditably. He was good-looking, and had nice manners; and Mrs. Innis was so complimentary that by the end of the week he believed himself the keenest man in the field. But as he grew in confidence he also became aware of the reputation which his mount enjoyed. He began to hint to Varick that Dooley was not a suitable horse for him.

"If I only had my prancer here," he observed, one morning, "you would see yoomping." Finally he told his host point-blank that, however well meant it might be, to give him such a tame mount as Dooley was no kindness; it was a reflection upon his equestrianism.

Then said Varick, who was annoyed, "You may ride Emperor tomorrow; but I tell you plainly that he may kill you." For the moment, he almost hoped he would.

"Fear not," said Cordillas, and thanked him much.

Varick says that he did *not* forget to tell William to have Emperor saddled for Cordillas. The head groom refuses to talk about it, but shakes his head. Those who know William hesitate to decide between him and his master, so the truth is likely to remain hid.

At the meet next morning, Cordillas flabbergasted the stable-boy who assisted him to mount by slipping a bill into his hand.

"An' 'im a halien," said the boy, as he related the matter to William. "Then 'e pats 'is neck, an' sez 'e, 'Ain't 'e a good 'un! Gawd! look at 'is fiery heye! This *is* a 'oss!' 'W'y, yes,' sez I; 'an' clipped yesterday, sir, which improves 'is looks uncommon. I might almost say, sir, one 'u'd scarcely know 'im.' Then 'e sez, 'Git up, Hemperor!' an' moves awfter 'em."

That day there was vouchsafed one of those "historic" runs which come usually when a man's best horse is laid up, or when he judges that the day is too dry for scent and stops at home. In the first covert the pack blundered on a fox, and burst wildly out of the woods, every hound giving tongue, and Reynard in full view, barely half a field away.

The men sat listening to the foxhounds' "music," half-eager bark, half-agonized yelp, with a fluttering of the pulses and a stirring of primeval instincts. The horses quivered and pawed, mouthed the bits, and tossed white slaver into the air. But the hounds had to get their distance; so the field held back, each man intently studying the far-off fence, and playing with the mouth of his restless horse. The excited Spaniard tugged on the curb, and his mount reared indignantly.

"Demon!" he shouted. A snicker rippled from the grooms in the rear.

"Good Lord!" exclaimed Varick. "He hasn't done that for eight years. Give him his head, man!"

At that instant the M. F. H. waved his hand, and the field charged across the meadow for the boards, over which the tail-end hounds were scrambling.

It was seven miles without a check to Christian's Mills, and the fox most of the time in view; then across the river, horses and hounds swimming together, and on again at a heartbreaking pace to Paddock's Gully, where they killed in the bottom. Three horses that went into the ravine were too pumped to get out again, and stayed there all night. In the memory of man such a run, without slow scent or check, had never been seen. It became the great after-dinner run of the Oakdale Hunt; and when they brag of their horses, they tell how, twice in the twelve miles, eleven men jumped five feet of stiff timber without breaking a rail.

In the last mile Cordillas followed the insane Braybrooke over four strands of naked wire that turned the field aside, beat him into the ravine, and was first at the death. They came upon him half buried in the yelping, panting pack which fought for the mangled fox he held over his head.

"Beat 'em off!" yelled Braybrooke. The reply was a torrent of Spanish oaths. Then the huntsman rode up, and rescued Cordillas, plastered with blood and filth, but content. He patted his mount's dripping neck.

"How magnificent a horse!" he exclaimed.

"Carried you extremely well," said Braybrooke. "Never saw the old fellow do better, or show so much speed. Great gallop, wasn't it? Let's have a pull at your flask; mine's dry."

"To the run," said the Spaniard, as he received the flask back, "and your good health!" He clutched the flask in his other hand.

"You rode well," said Braybrooke. His respect for the Latin races had increased. "The blood's dripping on your coat," he added, as Galloway came up, but Cordillas only held his trophy closer.

That night Varick had a man's dinner. There were toasts and healths, and bumpers to the five-foot fences, and perdition to the man who invented wire; bumpers to every good horse and man who was out that day; long life to hounds, and good luck to all hound puppies. But the Spaniard was the lion of the evening, and toward midnight there were cries of "speech!"

Cordillas rose cautiously, and stood facing the party, with a glass of champagne in his tremulous hand. He was touched, and his voice showed it. He thanked the company as a gentleman, as a Spaniard, and as a sportsman. He spoke in praise of his hosts' country, their women, and their bath-tubs. Then he got around to his prancer in

Madrid, and settled down to horses. To an equestrian like himself, he said, whose bosom throbbed in sympathy with every fiery impulse of creation's most noble animal, the fox-chase was the sport of kings. To a distinguished company of huntsmen he might well repeat the words of the English poet, with which they might be familiar, "My kingdom for a horse!" Developing his theme, he asserted that, of the various kinds of horses, the hunter was the noblest. "And of all noble hunters," he shouted, "the noblest, the fieriest, the most intrepid, I haf rode to-day! I drink to Emperor!"

At that moment Thomas Dooley, the newly clipped, was sniffing a bran mash, stiff and sore with the weariness born of his day's exertions under Cordillas y Sandoval. As every one at the table except the Spaniard knew, Emperor had not been out of his stall.

There was a moment's hush. The toast was drunk in silence. The men looked at one another, and then a tumult of cheers burst forth which set the grooms waiting at the stables to speculating upon the probable condition of their masters. To Cordillas it was an ovation, and the climax of his triumph. The tears stood in his eyes. To the Oakdale Hunt it was the only way of saving appearances and their good breeding.

"Keep the racket going," said Forbes to Braybrooke. "Don't let him know any one's laughing."

"I shall die of this," gasped Willie Colfax; and he slipped under the table, gurgling hysterically.

What else might have happened no one can say, because Charley Galloway started "For he's a jolly good fellow!" at the top of his lungs. Mrs. Galloway, who was sitting up for him in her own house half a mile down the road, says she recognized her husband's barytone. Every other man did the best that nature permitted. The Spaniard was reduced to tears, and the party recovered its gravity.

"But what is going to be the end of this?" whispered Varick to Chalmers. "If he catches on he will have me out, and kill me. And there's Mrs. Innis; oh, Lord! Reggie, you know everybody and all about everything in Washington; if you love me, get him back there."

Then Chalmers sent for his groom, and wrote some telegrams;

and the following afternoon Cordillas came to Varick, sorely cast down, and announced that the minister had sent him imperative orders to return.

"I fear," he said, "those infamous Cubaños have caused complications which necessitate my presence at the capital."

Varick said that he was awfully sorry—but saw to it personally that he caught the evening train. As it moved off, the Spaniard stood on the step and wrung his hand.

"My friend, possessor of that great horse Emperor," he said, "I thank you for the ride of my whole life."

"Please don't mention it," said Varick. "Don't speak of it!"

"But," he added to himself, "I am much afraid he will."

Old English Hunting Song

It's a fine hunting day
It's as balmy as May
The hounds to the village have come,
Every friend will be there
And all trouble and care
Will be left far behind us at home.

There's a fox in the spinny they say,
We'll find him and get him away,
I'll be first in the rush
And ride hard for the brush,
For I must go a hunting today.

There's a doctor in boots,
With a breakfast that suits,
Of good home-brewed ale and roast beef,
To his patients in pain
Who have come once again
To consult him in hopes of relief.
To the rich he prescribes they shall pay,
To the poor he advice gives away,
But to each one he said
You shall shortly be dead
If you don't go a hunting today.

Big Red

Arthur Bartlett

Any anthology of horses would be incomplete if the greatest of them all was not included. Particularly since he was as colorful as he was great. Man o' War was made for the headlines if ever a horse was.

Veteran horsemen have always maintained that the final test of true quality in a race horse is his ability to carry weight. Many horses are pure lightning when they are "carrying a feather," as the horseman has it, but under a heavier weight he may be only one of the "also rans."

In the handicaps for horses four years old and up, top weight is usually 130 pounds; and only then if there are really good horses in the field. Yet, as a two-year-old, Man o' War carried 130 pounds seven times! No other two-year-old has ever carried such weight. At three he carried 138 pounds; weight no three-year-old has ever carried. So, if this is the measuring rod, he stands by himself.

This account of his life appeared as a Profile in The New Yorker Magazine *while Big Red was still alive.*

In 1918, the race tracks of America were in the doldrums. The World War had engulfed the country; people were busy and preoccupied. Attendance at the races had slumped tremendously and purses, which are dependent on attendance, had shrunk proportionately. Major August Belmont, chairman of that ruling power of metropolitan turfdom, The Jockey Club, had retired from racing to devote himself to military service, and his trainer, Louis Feustel, had gone to work for Samuel D. Riddle, who was seizing this opportunity to build up his racing stable.

Man o' War.

Up to that time, Riddle had been one of the minor figures of the thoroughbred world. He and his wife, heiress of a Philadelphia textile-manufacturing fortune, had always been part of the hunt-club set outside of Philadelphia. He owned Glen Riddle Farm at Berlin, Maryland, and had raced a few fair-to-middling horses for years without any spectacular successes. A solid, expansive man, then approaching sixty, with the florid complexion of the sportsman and the easy assurance of the wealthy, he enjoyed the camaraderie of the turf's great—Whitneys, Wideners, Belmonts—without being quite of them. He needed horses that would bring more glory to his black-and-yellow colors. With that hope, he and Feustel went to the annual sale of yearlings at Saratoga in August, 1918, and bought two colts. One was named Gun Muzzle, the other Man o' War.

The colts were part of Major Belmont's crop of twenty-one yearlings bred at his Nursery Stud Farm at Lexington, Kentucky, and their militaristic names were a reflection of the Major's pre-occupation with the war. Before consigning them to the Saratoga sale, he had offered the whole lot to Riddle, at private sale, for $42,000—an average of $2,000 each. Riddle had declined, but he bid up to $5,000 for Man o' War when he went on the block. This was only in the middle range for the sale. Colts which never particularly distinguished themselves afterward brought prices ranging up to $14,000. Man o' War was a gangling, big-boned, long-legged golden chestnut, sired by Fair Play, a great money-winner. His dam, Mahubah, though of impressive bloodliness, had won only one paltry $700 purse in her entire racing career. Robert L. Gerry, who was the most persistent of those bidding against Riddle, thought of the colt as a good steeplechase prospect, because of his long legs. Many others at the ringside thought he was too big and awkward for a runner.

Feustel broke Man o' War that afternoon, in a paddock outside the Riddle stable at Saratoga. As soon as a jockey was lifted into the saddle, the colt gave a mighty buck and the jockey flew off. For fifteen minutes Man o' War pranced and bucked around the paddock. Finally, Feustel and his helpers caught him in a corner and held him until he quieted down. He never gave any trouble about being mounted after that.

To Feustel and his stable foreman, George Conway, Man o' War was just another colt. Feustel, then in his thirties, was one of the youngest trainers in the business. He had gone to work for Major Belmont at the age of eleven as a chore boy and had grown up among horses. Like most professional horsemen, he and Conway are taciturn, poker-faced men, who handle horses with as little emotion as a hardboiled hospital intern handles clinic patients. They shipped Man o' War with yearlings bought at other sales to the farm in Maryland, where he was ridden a bit each day to learn the meaning of the reins, walked in the walking ring, rubbed, washed, and put back in his stall. Occasionally, with the other colts, he was ridden in a sprint of an eighth or a quarter of a mile, under wraps, and it was in these sprints that he soon proved himself the most promising yearling on the farm, because of his long and powerful stride. In his prime, it was two feet longer than that of the average thoroughbred. Special notice began to be given to "Mahubah's colt," as he had been rather anonymously called, and the stableboys started calling him Big Red—all chestnut horses being red in the stable lexicon. He has been Big Red or just plain Red ever since to owner, trainers, jockeys, and grooms. Only strangers address him as Man o' War.

Adjoining Glen Riddle Farm in Maryland is the training farm of Mr. and Mrs. Walter M. Jeffords, the latter Riddle's niece, and the two racing establishments, while training and racing under separate colors, were always closely associated. One custom was to give the colts from the two farms their first real trials, after fall training in sets of two, one from each farm. Man o' War's first race was such a trial. A colt named Golden Broom had emerged as the year's favorite in the Jeffords string, and his handlers were sure that he could beat the big, awkward colt that the Riddle crowd talked so much about. They were right. The two colts were matched in the trials, Golden Broom got away fast, and Man o' War, slow in getting into his stride, never caught up.

"The twenty-eight foot stride."

With his reputation thus sullied, Big Red went into winter quarters. Nothing more in the way of speed was asked of him for the duration of cold weather; eating was his main job, and he took to it with so much greed that Feustel had to put a bit in his mouth at feeding time to keep him from bolting his food. That voracious appetite was one of his greatest assets. Many race horses get finicky about eating, and their condition suffers. Big Red has always loved to eat, and this accounts in large measure for his great strength and consistently rugged health.

He filled out that winter into a handsome two-year-old, deep-chested and with muscles that made his coat ripple. In spring training, he showed that he liked to run about as well as he liked to eat. The main trick of training is to bring a horse to the top of his efficiency at the right time, and the first workouts are light.

As the spring progressed, and Man o' War was worked harder and faster, he became so eager to turn on the speed that exercise boys had only to get into the saddle and hang onto the reins. A big brown hunter named Major Treat was the training pony at the farm, and it was his job to lead the high-strung thoroughbreds from the stable to the track, on the theory that his familiar, placid figure would be a calming influence and keep them from running away. As soon as the old decoy had been led off, Man o' War was always raring to go.

At Pimlico, early in the 1919 season, he had his first lesson in leaving the barrier, and track followers for the first time had reason to suspect that a colt named Man o' War was fast. A number of other promising colts were getting the same lesson that morning, and most of them broke away faster than Man o' War. But settling into his big stride, he rapidly overtook them, and had left them all behind at the quartermile mark. Johnny Loftus, the jockey who was riding for Riddle that year, liked the way Man o' War finished but was critical of the way he started. Loftus began working on him, trying to make him excited about getting away from the barrier fast and hitting his stride. Loftus was so successful that Man o' War developed into one of the most impetuous horses at the barrier in racing history, always so impatient to break away that he often delayed the starts by his rough behavior, and once held up a race for twelve minutes.

His first official race was at Belmont on June 6, 1919. It was one of those program-fillers that are arranged overnight, and the winner's share was $500. Few people remember the other starters in that race: Retrieve, Neddam, Devildog, Gladiator, Lady Brighton, American Boy. Man o' War's name meant nothing to most of the spectators, but the wise ones had heard enough about Riddle's promising colt to make him the favorite in the betting, at 3-5. He justified the odds by running away with the race, leaving his nearest competitor six lengths behind. Three days later he came out again, this time for the Keene Memorial, worth $4,200, and with stiffer competition. He streaked ahead of the field and led it home by three lengths. At Jamaica, two weeks later, he won his third race, and two days after that he was at Aqueduct winning his fourth. His next appearance was in the Tremont Stakes at Aqueduct, a three-quarter-mile race. He won that by a length. The next month, at Saratoga, he won the important United States Hotel Stakes, worth $7,600, his sixth consecutive victory.

By this time, Man o' War was distinctly a sensation. His groom, Frank Loftus (no relation to his jockey), was warned never to let him out of sight during his working hours. In the evenings, Feustal, Conway, and their friends set up a table in front of his stall for a nightly game of pitch. When the game was over, Conway went to bed right next to the stall. After every race, Feustel examined the horse minutely, to make sure that he had not been cut or scratched. Andy McDermott, the stable's blacksmith, fitted his shoes with special care, though Big Red never needed anything but regulation plates. Clyde Gordon, the ex-jockey who exercised him, was the envy of every swipe in the stable. Yet his was a strenuous job, for Man o' War, gentle as a cow in his stall, was transformed into a dynamo as soon as he was out. Jockey Loftus took over the job of exercising him one morning and had one of the wildest rides of his career. Breaking out of a jog, the colt reared on his hind legs until he stood nearly erect, then bounded at least five feet in the air, took two more great leaps, and settled down to run a half mile in 47 seconds. The world's record is 46 1/5. Loftus, one of the most experienced jockeys of the day, was white and shaking when he got back to the stable.

People were beginning to talk about Man o' War as unbeatable, but there were still many who doubted it. With the competition getting more keen as the season went on, Man o' War, because of his previous victories, would have to carry more weight than the newcomers. Harry Payne Whitney's trainer, Jimmy Rowe, was sure he could win with a colt named Upset, whom Man o' War had beaten in his last race, and Mike Daly, the Jeffords trainer, still had faith in Golden Broom, whom he had recently been bringing on. On August 13th, Man o' War was to meet Golden Broom and one of the Whitney colts, Upset, in the Sanford Memorial at Saratoga. Mrs. Riddle, who had been coming from Pennsylvania for all Man o' War's races, showed her scorn for the challengers by planning a party and having a cake made with Man o' War's name in fancy frosting for the victory celebration.

Man o' War was the favorite in the betting, 1–2. At the barrier, he began cutting up as usual—or worse than usual. The regular starter had been replaced temporarily by an assistant, and when the assistant gave the word to start, Man o' War was turned almost completely in the wrong direction. Jockey Loftus headed him around, but not until four of the other horses were away ahead of him. Upset took the lead, but Golden Broom passed him and led at the half-mile mark by a head, setting a terrific pace. Man o' War struggled to break through the mass formation of flying hoofs, but succeeded in passing only one horse in the first half-mile. Loftus did not move him to the outside of the track; apparently he meant to find a hole through which to maneuver. But Man o' War was still blocked as they approached the stretch. Only then did Loftus move him outside. It was a stupendous task that he was asking of the colt—to go out around the leaders in that short remaining distance. But Big Red undertook it. He passed two of the four horses as soon as the track was clear ahead of him. Up front, Golden Broom was wilting and Upset was taking the lead. Man o' War roared on, left

Golden Broom behind, drew up on Upset. His nose was just passing Upset's flank as they crossed the finish line. Three or four more powerful strides, and Man o' War flashed by—too late.

It was the only official race he ever lost, and track followers still argue about it. Some blame Loftus for bad judgement or worse; others insist he just didn't have racing luck that day. Riddle let him ride Man o' War's remaining three races of the season, but next year The Jockey Club refused to renew his licence.

Man o' War's other three races that year included The Futurity at Belmont, with a winner's share of $26,650. He won them all handily, before increasingly big crowds. Nearly every major track drew more people that year than in the ten years past. The Futurity drew one of the greatest crowds that had ever come to Belmont Park. As evidence of Man o' War's part in drawing them there, so many pressed into the paddock as he came out, trying to get a more intimate glimpse of him, that his handlers could hardly push through the mob.

Feustel and Conway by now were actually fussing over the horse—in an undemonstrative, horsemanlike way. His first meal was at 3:30 in the morning. Then he took it easy in his stall until 7:30, when Frank Loftus, his groom, massaged him with a hairbrush, went over his mane and tail with a corn brush, washed his feet and face, and sponged out his eyes and nostrils. At 8:30, half the horses in the stable had been exercised, and Man o' War went out with the second set. Three days a week he jogged half a mile and galloped a mile and a half. Tuesdays, Thursdays, and Saturdays he was given fast workouts on the track. After these workouts, he was walked until he had cooled out, then bathed with a mixture of alcohol, arnica, and witch hazel to keep his muscles from getting stiff. His feet and hoofs were washed again and the bandages which he always wore except when racing were changed. Then he was put back in his stall, which had been cleaned and covered with fresh straw. At 11:30 he had lunch. At 4 he was led out for a half-hour's walk and at 5:15 he got his final meal of the day. His total consumption of oats was twelve quarts on ordinary days, twelve and a half on the days he raced—three quarts a day more than that of the average race horse in training.

After The Futurity, Phil Chinn and Montford Jones, two Southern breeders, offered Riddle $100,000 for Man o' War. He turned the offer down without a second thought. The colt had now become one of the most valuable pieces of horseflesh in the world.

The 1920 season went far beyond that of 1919 in attendance at the tracks, breaking all records. And Man o' War was the great hero. At every race, the crowds surged around him so densely that cordons of police had to make way for him to get to and from the tracks. Sportswriters, all through the season, kept coupling his name with that of Babe Ruth as one who was reviving a waning sport by lusty and colorful performances. Riddle, excited and eager for ever-greater triumphs, began holding what the newspapers termed "board of strategy" meetings with his friends and even with track kibitzers to discuss the races in which Man o' War should be started and how the jockey should be instructed to ride. Feustel, temperamental and proud of his part in the horse's career, resented this as meddling in his field. The result was a series of minor squabbles. Feustel was particularly annoyed when he discovered that despite the careful watch he and his helpers kept over Man o' War, Riddle had hired a private detective to watch *them*. Man o' War's triumphs overshadowed such petty matters for the time being, but Riddle and Feustel parted company as soon as the horse stopped racing.

Clarence Kummer, a jockey who had made a good record the year before, was engaged to succeed Loftus as Man o' War's rider for the 1920 season. He got $1,000 for each race he rode, except the final one of the year for which he got $5,000. Man o' War's first start that year was in The Preakness at Pimlico. His old rival—and only conqueror—Upset was also entered, and Man o' War beat him by a length and a half. Then he went on winning race after race, regardless of distance, weight, or competition. After his first appearance of the season, when he was a 4–5 favorite, the odds on him dropped steadily until they reached an all-time low of 1–100 in his fourth race. It began to be taken for granted that he would win, and betting almost stopped. Nobody wanted to bet against him, and at the odds there was little to be made in betting on him. "Chicago" O'Brien, an ex-bricklayer who had gambled his way to a million-dollar fortune, did succeed in making $1,000 on him in the Belmont Stakes. He did it by putting up $100,000. Man o' War won the race by twenty lengths.

Owners began scratching their entries in his races for no other reason than that Man o' War was running. In his first race of 1920, eight other hopeful three-year-olds started, but after that three was the most that ever came to the post against him, and in six of his eleven races that year he had only one contestant. Horsemen don't like to see their most promising horses beaten; many of them think it "breaks their hearts." And with one or two exceptions they had no hope of beating Man o' War that year; second money was the only lure.

Only once that season was Big Red even pushed. Harry Payne Whitney and his trainer, Rowe, were still hopeful of beating him. They had lost with Upset, but their trump card was a horse named John P. Grier, whom they had been carefully bringing along for a meeting with Man o' War in the Dwyer at Aqueduct. Many horsemen say that the resulting race was the greatest ever run. For a mile the two horses raced virtually even, matching stride for stride. When they passed the mile post they had equalled the world's record of 1:35 4/5. There was only an eighth of a mile more to go. At this point, John P. Grier stuck his nose out ahead and the crowd roared, certain that Man o' War—"the Wonder Horse of the Century," as the newspapers now called him—was beaten. Kummer pulled the whip, and Big Red felt its sting for one of the few times in his life. He leaped forward. Less than a hundred yards from the finish, he pulled ahead. He crossed the line a length and a half ahead.

In his other races, he was almost always being pulled up at the finish, his lead safe. By the time the Lawrence Realization came along, late in the season, it began to look as if Man o' War would have to run all by himself. Only one horse had been entered against him, and his owner thought better of it and scratched him. To save the day, Mrs. Jeffords entered one of her horses, Hoodwink, and Kummer was instructed to hold Red back as much as he could, so the Jeffords horse would not look too bad. Kummer rode the whole race pulling on the reins and Man o' War gave Hoodwink one of the worst beatings ever administered on a major race track, leaving him a full hundred lengths behind. The photographers had to aim their cameras straight up the stretch to get him into the same picture with the winner.

The final race of the season, and of Man o' War's career, was a special match at Kenilworth, Canada, with a famous four-year-old, Sir Barton, for $75,000 and a gold cup. Winning by seven lengths, Man o' War cost the track a lot of money when he paid $2.10 for $2, the shortest odds possible under the Canadian laws. Thousands of dollars had poured in, actually making the odds much shorter than they showed in the payoff.

The day before the race, Man o' War breezed a quarter-mile in a workout. Various track followers clocked him, as they are always doing at workouts. The slowest time any of them caught was 21 1/5 seconds, and others insisted that he went the distance in 20 2/5. In any event, as motorists figure speed, he was touching somewhere around forty-three miles an hour, and it was faster than any other horse has ever been known to run, with or without competition. In most of his races he could have made faster time than he did—his jockeys were usually restraining him. Nevertheless, he set five new American records. His time of 2:14 1/5 for a mile and three-eighths, under 126 pounds, established in the Belmont Stakes, still stands as both the American and world record. His Lawrence Realization time of 2:40 4/5 (despite being restrained all the way) under 126 pounds stands as the American record for a mile and five-eighths. He also is co-holder with Sir Barton of the track record for a mile and a quarter at Saratoga—2:01 4/5. He had in two years raced and beaten the fifty best horses of his age and, in Sir Barton, one of the best of the older horses then racing. He had won $249,465. It made him the biggest money-winner of American racing up to that time. Since then, with track patronage having reached new highs, the same races which he won have paid much more, and other horses have won more money than he did. He stands fifteenth in the world's money-winning list now, but if each of his races paid as much as it had paid since then, he would still be at the top of the list, with a total of around $600,000.

Riddle could have doubled the amount that the horse had made him if he had been willing to sell him then. The late W. T. Waggoner, owner of the Arlington Downs track in Texas, offered him $250,000. He turned it down, as he did an offer of a $100,000 purse for a race in England, made by Freeman Bernstein, a New York promoter, and other propositions of a similar size. He was besieged with offers to put Man o' War on exhibition and into the movies. One movie proposal almost reached the stage of signing papers, and Feustel, who was to be signed, too, was irritated anew at his employer when Riddle finally turned it down. "They were going to write a villain into the story," says Riddle, "and there aren't any villains in Man o' War's story." Riddle did consent to an exhibition among his friends and neighbors at the Rose Tree Hunt, just outside of Philadelphia. Jack Dempsey and Bill Tilden were among the hundreds who traveled out there to see the horse. Souvenir hunters clipped so much hair off his mane and tail that the Philadelphia police sent a sergeant and ten men to guard him.

After that, Riddle shipped him down to Lexington, Kentucky. He went, as he had gone to his more recent races, with only his old companion, Major Treat, as equine company in the horsecar. It was just such a conveyance as those in which he had always traveled—a horsecar with straw on the floor, chartered for the journey; but whereas such a car will accommodate eighteen horses, Man o' War had become too important to be crowded. At Lexington, he ran an exhibition mile at the track, with Major Treat pacing him, then was retired, definitely and permanently. He might have gone on to win many more races. Horsemen of this generation will argue about that until they die. A good many think that Man o' War's legs were going back on him and that he wouldn't have been much of a four-year-old. Others say that he would have been a great one but that the handicappers would have broken him down. In his next-to-the-last race, when he cracked the track record for a mile and a sixteenth at Havre de Grace, he carried 138 pounds, which is only a few pounds less than any American handicapper has asked a horse to carry in modern flat racing. Inevitably his handicap would have been stiffer that next season. One thing is sure: Riddle wanted Big Red to retire a champion, and that is what Big Red was when he quit racing.

Man o' War's place of retirement is Faraway Farms, a few miles north of Lexington. Except for a short stay at another stud farm while Riddle built this one, he has been there ever since his racing career ended. His stud fee is $5,000, and he has been bred to twenty-five mares each year. His total registered get was 277 up to last January [1938]. Of these 236, or about eighty per cent, had started in races—a high average. Among the best have been Mars, Crusader, Genie, Scapa Flow, American Flag, Clyde Van Dusen, Edith Cavell, Bateau, and this year's sensation, War Admiral. Altogether, his sons and daughters have won $2,400,000. Riddle, however, has grown more and more sentimental about Man o' War and refuses to discuss him in financial terms, insisting that it would be virtually sacrilegious. He wants the horse considered a public institution rather than a business venture. And to some extent he has managed him on this theory; several times he has waved the $5,000 stud fee when he thought some particularly good result might come from breeding him to a mare whose owner could not pay the price. Nevertheless, Man o' War has probably made over a million dollars for him in prize money, stud fees, and sale of foals. That does not take into account the money that Riddle has won with sons and daughters of Man o' War, and he has bred him to his own mares more than to outsiders, and has kept more foals than he has sold. Whether or not this has been to his profit is questionable; many foals which would have brought good prices on Man o' War's name alone have failed to develop and have had to be written off as a loss. On the other hand, the big winners, like their sire, go on making money as progenitors of more horses for years after they leave the tracks. Man o' War, as keystone and controlling factor of this continuing family, has made Riddle one of the great men of the turf. The $5,000 he paid for the colt is probably the most sensational investment in turf history.

Nearing eighty now, Riddle has recently built a small house just a few steps from Man o' War's barn, where he and Mrs. Riddle can go for a few days or weeks occasionally to be near the founder of their racing fortunes. It pleases Riddle that people still drive out to see the horse just as much as they did when he first retired—three thousand a month come, on the average, except in the winter—and he likes to talk to the visitors about the horse and to share, with a deprecatory gesture, his glory.

Man o' War was twenty years old last March [1938]. That is old age for a horse, but his life is little changed from what it was when he first went to the stud. His weight has increased from 1,000 pounds to around 1,375, and the fine racing lines have given way to a slightly potbellied appearance, but he is still strong and vigorous, and still likes to run. He lives in a box stall twenty feet square, which is always covered a foot deep with straw. Three similar box stalls fill up the rest of the stud stable; two of them are occupied by Big Red's sons, Crusader and American Flag, and the third now stands vacant, waiting for the time when War Admiral will retire to the stud. Other horses have come and gone. Among them was Golden Broom, Big Red's early rival, but Golden Broom wilted and lost this race to Man o' War, as he had lost the other: he died in 1935. Man o' War shows no signs of senility. From the first of October until the close of the breeding season, late in June, he is under saddle. Just as in his racing days, he is worked up to the peak of condition by a gradual increase in exercise—first walking and jogging, then getting up to galloping six to eight miles a day. And at the end of the season he is "unwound," just as he used to be, by a tapering off exercise. He has a private two-acre paddock in which to ramble as he pleases—all day if the sun is not too hot, otherwise at night. Out there, he plays with the farm dogs, challenging them to come in, then chasing them out. He eats three times a day—at five o'clock, eleven, and four. At each meal he gets three quarts of heavy rolled oats. His hay, a mixture of red clover and timothy, is shipped from Michigan; his green food is the Kentucky blue grass in his paddock. He is just about the biggest stallion in the blue-grass country, and he would eat even more if he could get it; he has never lost his appetite. His retinue now consists of his Negro groom, Will Harbutt; Will's son Robert, who rides him; a stableman, and a night watchman. Insured for $500,000, he is under the eye of one of these men every minute. Most of the time during the day Harbutt or one of the others is in the barn or standing outside. They have a room in an adjoining building, in which they can go when it is cold; it has extra large windows which command a view of the side door of the barn, and the front door at such times is locked on the inside. If visitors appear, a man is quickly at their side, ready to show them around, but watchful. At four o'clock visiting hours are over, and at five the night watchman comes on duty, and stays until the others return at five in the morning.

Big Red's old companions of racing days are scattered now. Feustel, training horses in Maryland, has gradually faded into the background of the turf, waiting in vain for some horse even approaching Man o' War's stature to lift him again into the lime-light and the big money. Conway, the former stable foreman, is Riddle's trainer now but he seldom gets to the stud farm. Of the jockeys, Kummer is dead and Loftus is a trainer in the North. Frank Loftus, the old groom, moves from track to track, caring for other horses. But the old warrior is still the "Wonder Horse of the Century." Signposts on the roads outside Lexington point the way to his home. In 1934 the sculptor Herbert Haseltine came from Paris to immortalize him in bronze and gold plate. And every once in a while some new attempt is made to lure him away from the blue grass to appear before a public that still lionizes him. The last big offer was for an appearance at the Century of Progress Exposition.

Riddle will never let Big Red leave Faraway Farms. And to ask any question which suggests that the horse sometime will die means sure banishment from Riddle's presence. Will Harbutt, in showing him off to visitors, always takes them first to see each of the other horses in the stable and recites their triumphs. Then he leads the way to the big chestnut stallion. There is a trace of the courtier in him as he waves his arm, a trace of the side-show barker. "And heah," he announces triumphantly, "is Man o' War *hisself!*"

Man o' War vs Upset

Willie Knapp

Man o' War's only defeat has been the subject of much discussion for it is clear to all horsemen that he towered over all his opposition. This is the true version of that race from the man who saw it all, close up, Willie Knapp, the rider on Upset that day. Here it is in his own words as told to a turf writer.

There were seven horses in the Sanford, with Man o' War held at eleven to twenty odds, but when the field bounced away it was Golden Broom settin' the pace, with Upset on the outside, just a neck away. Man o' War didn't make his bid till we hit the turn, and then he churned up along the rail till his head bobbed into the corner of my eye. There he was, tossin' those twenty-eight foot strides of his an' tryin' to squeeze through on the inside of Golden Broom and Upset. If I'd given as much as an inch the race would've been as good as over, but jockeys don't ride that way. I could have breezed past Golden Broom any time I took my feet out of the dashboard but that would have let Man o' War out of his mouse-trap and he'd have whooshed past us in half a dozen strides.

"When Johnny Loftus, ridin' Man o' War, saw we weren't going to open up, there was only one thing left for him to do. He pulled up sharply and ducked to the outside. That's what I'd been waiting for. That same moment I gunned Upset with my bat and galloped to the top in a pair of jumps. Man o' War then had to come out around the two of us and it cost him all of two lengths. From there to the finish he was chargin' again like a jet plane but Upset had just enough left to push his head down in front."

"Then you think," he was asked, "that Man o' War was the best horse that afternoon?"

"He could do anything—and do it better than any horse that ever lived."

"And every other afternoon, too. Just take a gander at the records. Upset never beat him again. Big Red came back to win the Hopeful, the Futurity, the Grand Union and twenty outa twenty-one races in all, with Upset never again close enough to smell his dust.

"Sure, I won the race all right—it was the biggest thrill o' my life—but lookin' back at it now there's sure one horse which shoulda retired undefeated. Never saw a colt like him. He could do anything—and do it better than any horse that ever lived. If I'd moved over just an eyelash that day at Saratoga he'd have beat me from here to Jaloppy. Sometimes I'm sorry I didn't do it."

Right Royal

John Masefield

John Masefield was never a horseman, but fox hunting fascinated him, and his feeling for horses was as strong as that of many died-in-the-wool horsemen, or he could never have written the long, dramatic poem, Right Royal. *In fact, it is hard for me to believe that anyone who had not taken care of his own horse could have written the selection below. It is said that Masefield did all his fox hunting from a bicycle or on foot, which is not uncommon in England, but if so, he had an eye and an ear granted very few men. (–From* Right Royal)

Just at the grey of dawn I had a dream.
It was the strangest dream I ever had.
It was the dream that drove me to be mad.

I dreamed I stood upon the race-course here,
Watching a blinding rainstorm blowing clear,
And as it blew away, I said aloud,
'That rain will make soft going on the ploughed.'
And instantly I saw the whole great course,
The grass, the brooks, and fences topped with gorse,
Gleam in the sun; and all the ploughlands shone
Blue, like a marsh, though now the rain had gone.
And in my dream I said, 'That plough will be
Terrible work for some, but not for me.
Not for Right Royal.'
        And a voice said 'No,
Not for Right Royal.'

And I looked and, lo!
There was Right Royal, speaking, at my side.
The horse's very self, and yet his hide
Was like, what shall we say? like pearl on fire,
A soft white glow of burning that did twire
Like soft white-heat with every breath he drew.
A glow, with utter brightness running through;
Most splendid, though I cannot make you see.

His great crest glittered as he looked at me
Criniered with spitting sparks; he stamped the ground
All cock and fire, trembling like a hound,
And glad of me, and eager to declare
His horse's mind.
    And I was made aware
That, being a horse, his mind could only say
Few things to me. He said, 'It is my day,
My day, to-day; I shall not have another.'

And as he spake he seemed a younger brother
Most near, and yet a horse, and then he grinned
And tossed his crest and crinier to the wind,
And looked down to the Water with an eye
All fire of soul to gallop dreadfully.

All this was strange, but then a stranger thing
Came afterwards. I woke all shivering
With wonder and excitement, yet with dread
Lest the dream meant that Royal should be dead,
Lest he had died and come to tell me so.
I hurried out, no need to hurry, though;
There he was shining like a morning star.
Now hark. You know how cold his manners are,
Never a whinny for his dearest friend.
To-day he heard me at the courtyard end,
He left his breakfast with a shattering call,
A View Halloo, and, swinging in his stall,
Ran up to nuzzle me with signs of joy.
It staggered Harding and the stable-boy,
And Harding said, 'What's come to him today?
He must have had a dream he beat the bay.'

Cowboy

Ross Santee

Ross Santee studied for several years at the Art Institute of Chicago. He loved the out-of-doors and all sports, and the meticulous copying of plaster casts that was required of him at the Art Institute did not suit him. A short period in New York was even more depressing to him and he went to Arizona to work on a large cattle spread. He was through with art.

As he told me later, he first began to make small, rough sketches on his leather chaps with a burnt-out match—sketches of a horse or a steer or anything that interested him. These could be rubbed out as on a slate, but some of the cowhands saw them.

On a trip to town they looked for art materials for him, but the best they could get was ink and brush from a Chinese laundry. Thus began his brush style that freed him from the detailed drawing that he hated.

Eventually he was persuaded to send some of his brush sketches back East and they became popular at once. Their vigor and directness were something new.

He returned to New York and wrote and illustrated stories of the West for many leading magazines. Ross's stories all evolved from what he had seen or heard. Of a late afternoon he would come to my studio, squat on his heels and roll innumerable Bull Durham cigarettes; then would come a story, full of life, completely authentic.

Perhaps a day or two later he would drop in again, and again he would tell the story—perhaps slightly changed. Sometimes even a third time. Then some night he would work until daylight and it would be ready for the editor. (—From Cowboy)

I've seen Mack spend an hour just foolin' with a bronc. He would tie one hind foot. An' put the blanket on an' pull it off, an' rub the old pony with it, until the bronc finally got it through his head he wasn't goin' to be hurt. Then he'd put the saddle on an' pull it off, till the bronc got used to it. Then first thing the old bronc knew, Mack had took the foot-ropes off an' was sittin' on his back. Most of them pitched at first. But Mack never spurred or whipped a horse unless he needed it. Most horses is mighty quick to learn if a man knows how to handle them, an' any time you see a horse that's spoilt you can usually trace it back to some puncher that has rode him. Whenever Mack got through with one it wasn't a one-man horse.

It's as natural for a bronc to fight an' pitch at first, as it is for a duck to swim. That's the only weapon a pony has, an' he's only tryin' to protect himself, for at first he's scared to death. Of course, there's always some you can't be easy on. An' they whip it out of them. Then again you'll find a bronc that will never give up, an' the more a puncher fights him the more he fights back. For horses is just like humans, an' each of them has different ways. An' there's a heap of difference between breakin' one and ridin' in a contest. Some people who can ride most anythin' ain't fit to break a horse. An' on a ranch, whenever you find a peeler that's rough, he's always given horses that fight him back an' play the same game he does.

Around a horse outfit where they're snappin' broncs there's always some man hurt. Some peelers is just unlucky. Joe had the same leg broke three times while I was workin' there; an' Tex was laid up a half dozen times—while Mack was never hurt.

The peelers kidded me a lot about that eye of mine. But it wasn't long before I learned to ride. For as soon as the punchers let the hammer down on some new bronc, they'd let me try him out. At first they picked out ones that didn't pitch so hard, an' as I kept doin' better they give me tougher ones. I couldn't reach none of their stirrups by a foot. An' I got plenty of falls. "Want to try this one, kid?" they'd say, an' any time McDougal wasn't anywheres

"There's hardly a day I wasn't on some bucking horse."

around I'd crawl up in the saddle. I was mighty lucky, too. For there's hardly a day I wasn't on some buckin' horse. An' besides a long cut over my right eye, a broken nose was all I had to show for the first six months I rode.

I'd been there most six months I guess, an' I was pretty cocky. I'd tried every horse they'd let me on, an' I hadn't been bucked off in most two weeks, when they caught up a little black an' told me I could ride him.

"You can use your own saddle too," Mack says. "An' instead of toppin' him off in one of the smaller corrals you can ride him in the big one."

That suited me, an' Mack held the black while I laced my saddle on. Joe an' Tex both stood around with some blankets in their hands. Mack eared the black horse down an' waited till I got all set.

"Let's see a real ride this time," says Tex.

"Take your hat off an' start right in on him first jump. All set?" Mack says.

I said I was an' Mack turned the pony loose. Tex an' Joe both throwed their blankets under him so I didn't get to fan. For the old bronc made about four jumps that was so high an' wide it was all I could do to keep my seat. I was pullin' leather by the time we went into the fence, an' the old bronc hit that fence on high. Next thing I knowed I was layin' in the shade an' the boys was workin' over me. But the minute I set up an' looked around Mack says, "Mebbe, your hat will fit you now." An' then the whole bunch laughed.

My nose felt pretty sore for several days, an' both my eyes were black. But Mack was right about my hat, for I was fairly quiet for a spell. I was afraid if McDougal should happen in he would fire me then an' there, for he had told me several times to keep off them bad horses. McDougal had wrote to dad an' told him where I was. An' dad had wrote back an' said I hadn't run away. I imagine McDougal had some idea of what was goin' on, for several times he said to me:

"Stay off them broncs, Button, for you're a long ways from home."

We hadn't seen the old man for a month when one night he come

Ross Santee first began to make small, rough sketches on his leather chaps with a burnt-out match. Later he worked with ink and brush from a Chinese laundry—the only art materials available to him in Arizona at that time.

a drivin' in. Tex an' Joe was laid up right then, an' I was in the room with them. It was after supper an' Mack an' the old man was talkin' in his room. Finally I heard the old man say to Mack that if some light rider come along to put him on, for he wanted some young colts broke. An' then I most quit breathin', for I heard Mack say, "Why don't you put Button on?"

"They'd kill that kid," the old man says. "He don't know how to ride."

"The deuce he don't," says Mack. "He's been ridin' for six months, an' ridin' tough horses too."

The old man never said no more to that, an' I eased outside the house. I had to let off steam some way, an' I thought the thing was fixed. For while I was down a-talkin' to White Man on the flat I saw his lights go out.

Next mornin' the old man never had a word to say, in spite of the fact that I took plenty of pains to let him know that I was there. For I was busier than a coon dog all about the place, an' I swept the whole place out before it started breakin' light—except the room where Tex an' Joe was, an' they wouldn't stand for that.

It was while I was feedin' the chickens that the old man spoke to me. An' when he spoke it was like havin' cold water throwed all over me.

"Thought I told you to stay off them broncs," he said a-lookin' at me real hard.

"You did," I says, "but I won't do it any more if you jest let me stay."

With that the old man grunted an' stroked his white mustache. "I might have expected it," he says, "but as long as you've gone an' learned to ride, I'll tell you what I'll do. There's a bunch of colts I want broke. Mack will show you the ones."

"That suits me fine," I says, an' if the old man hadn't been a-standin' there, I'd have gone to turnin' flips.

"Another thing," he says, "I'll raise your wages too. I can't pay you as much as the other boys, but I'll give you twenty a month. An' I'll buy you another saddle, for that one of yours is no good."

At that the old man walked inside the house an' left me standin'

there. The minute he was gone I beat it for the corrals to tell Mack
of my good luck. Mack sort of grinned, but he was never much on
talk. Joe an' Tex was both a-playin' pitch, an' after I told them I
hunted White Man up.

He always grazed around the ranch an' he never did go far, an'
the minute I showed up he always raised his head as if there was
somethin' up, an' usually there was.

"White Man," I says, "You may not know it, but I'm a-gettin'
on."

BRONCS AND PEELERS

Mack put one on awhile we called 'Pretty Dick.' But we never used
the handle when he happened to be near. He come along one night
not long after Joe an' Dave had quit, a-ridin' a big, good-lookin'
horse with lots of pretties on his rig. But the average peeler is long
on that, so we paid no heed to it. Mack talked to him awhile an'
finally put him on. He wasn't as good a hand as Mack or Tex, but
there's no denyin' he could ride.

At first he talked enough but not too much. But nothin' ever
quite suited him. I always got steamed up when Mack or Tex made
a real good ride, but he always laid the heavy stone on me.

"Pretty good," he'd say, but he didn't like some little thing in the
way they handled a horse.

He had rode from Canada to Old Mexico, an' he had a way of
tellin' it as if Mack an' Tex was hicks. He had never rode for
anythin' except real big spreads. An' he'd tell of some outfit where
he'd worked, an' how they done, in a way that would make me feel
like we was herdin' goats. Yep, he never just said so in as many
words, but he was doin' us all a favor by just a-workin' here.
Naturally, it all went down with me at first.

Another thing he was always talkin' on—he had never fixed no
fence or ever worked none on the ground. Mack an' Tex both split
the milkin' up with me, an' they'd help do everythin'. An' most of
the peelers who come along acted just the way they did. An' there

was plenty of peelers who happened along, too, that wasn't too proud to milk. For we wasn't peddlin' out the stuff. An' most peelers wasn't slow to say how good it was after usin' the stuff in cans. But Pretty was too proud to milk.

The talk at night around a ranch is mostly of the work that day. An' the horses is all rode over plenty of times while the men is settin' around. It was always funny to hear Tex or Mack. They were both top hands, an' knowed it too, but they never took themselves too serious. There was always plenty of laughs from them whenever they told a thing.

But Pretty Dick had a way of tellin' a thing as if bronc ridin' started with him. He shore was full of words all right. An' after I'd listen for a while about some ride he made, or how he had handled a certain horse, I'd begin to wonder if he didn't have somethin' up his sleeve I didn't get, although I'd seen the ride. Once I spoke of it to Mack.

"He's good, all right," Mack says, "for after I hear him talk awhile I begin to wonder how we ever got along until that bird showed up."

It happened one mornin' in the corral, what I'd been hopin' for. Pretty had crawled a big sorrel that was too much horse for him. An' the sorrel horse spread Pretty all over the corral. Pretty Dick's face was white an' drawn when he crawled back on again. I'm not belittlin' his ridin' an' don't think he wasn't game. But the sorrel was naturally too much horse for him an' he busted Pretty again.

We drug him over in the shade an' soon as he set up Mack says if Pretty don't mind he'd try the horse himself. Pretty looked rather peaked, but he never said a word.

"Chances is good he'll throw me too," Mack says. Then he winked at me an' Tex. "For I've never been around, an' me an' Tex is just a couple of lint-backs [cotton-pickers] that is doin' the best we can, an' it's always been our luck to work for some Jim Crow outfit instead of the big spreads."

Pretty got just what he meant, for his face turned white as chalk. Then Mack crawled up on the sorrel without even changin' saddles.

I've seen plenty of rides since then, for that was long ago. But

"And every jump the sorrel took Mack raked him with his spurs."

I've never seen a real one since that I don't think back to it. For the sorrel was a big, stout horse, which would weigh twelve hundred pounds. Pretty had screwed down in the cinch with both his spurs, an' he'd pulled all the leather there was in sight, an' still the sorrel had unloaded him.

But the first thing Mack done the minute he stepped acrost was to reach way up an' hook the sorrel in the shoulders an' hit him with his hat. I'd never seen Mack spur a horse like that, an' he often spoke to me about tearin' a pony up. "We're not contestin'," he'd say. "We're hired to break a horse an' learn him everything we can, without half killin' him."

The sorrel made several jumps before he turned on good. Every time he hit the ground we could hear the leathers pop. But Mack still raked him with his spurs. "Show me somethin', sorrel horse," Mack finally yelled at him. "I'm just a pore old country boy a-tryin' to get on."

Somethin' choked up inside of me an' I couldn't say nothing.

"Oh, you ridin' fool!" yells Tex, an' then he begun to cuss.

An' the sorrel horse still wiped it up, with Mack still deep in the wood. An' every jump the sorrel took he raked him with his spurs.

Finally the big jolts begun to slacken, an' he didn't hit so hard. But Mack was still rakin' him when the sorrel's head come up. The sorrel stood there shakin' when Mack stepped off to the ground. An' Mack was shakin' some himself, an' his face was awful white. Mack pulled the saddle off the sorrel, an' he never said a word until I went to turn the horse outside.

"You can have him, Button," he says then. "He'll be a good horse for you to ride when you drive the milk cows up."

We all went in the house an' eat, an' Mack never said no more. Pretty was quiet too, until Mack an' Tex had gone outside. But while I was washin' the dishes he explained it all to me an' just how he got throwed. The sorrel wasn't much of a horse, he says, an' he'd rode lots tougher ones. I didn't say much, but it wasn't goin' down with me. An' as soon as I got the dishes washed I hunted up Mack and Tex.

When I told them what Pretty had said, Tex started in to cuss.

But Mack just laughed about it; then he finally says:

"Pride is a good thing, Button, an' I wouldn't give two bits for a man who didn't have lots of pride. But any man who lets his pride just swaller him is ridin' for a fall."

Colts in Pasture

Billy B. Cooper

Young colts in pasture are small Satans loosed
Upon resilient turf in morning hours;
Hoofs thudding rhythmically and bristled manes
Flung leeward; stubby tails that arch and curve
Halfway to flying hocks. Young colts can be
A squealing drove of bold rascality
In early morning; but when noontime nears,

Knees buckle sodward, ears droop forward, flick
A time or two as, stretched full length in sun
Sleek bays and chestnuts, roans and sorrels dream
Of clover fields with running brooks knee deep;
Small foals at noontide fallen fast asleep.
Young colts in pasture when the dusk dips low
Are bands of angels, four-footed, lingering near
The brood mares, nickering plaintively,
As one by one they seek their mother's side
And trot obediently through barnyard gate;
Small colts are cherubs when the hour grows late.

Eddie Arcaro and Whirlaway

Eddie Arcaro

Eddie Arcaro was one of our greatest jockeys—many think the greatest. He was not only a great rider but a fine horseman. He studied the horses he rode and learned all their characteristics and idiosyncrasies. Many riders had tried to keep the unpredictable Whirlaway to a straight course but none succeeded until Arcaro was called upon. Trainers have said that Arcaro could step down from a horse he had just galloped for the first time and tell them things about him that they, themselves, had not yet discovered.

He was a rugged competitor and sometimes ran afoul of the men who stood in the judges' stand, but never for "not trying." When he came whipping and pumping down the stretch, the boys soon learned to give him racing room. "Don't block Arcaro!" was the watchword. (—From I Ride to Win)

(TELEGRAM)

Jockey Eddie Arcaro:
Don't fail to be here stop I think we have the best chance of any in the race stop Don't pay any attention to race today stop He should have won by ten lengths stop I have a room for you Wire me when to meet you

Ben A Jones

Jones would never engage a rider for one of his horses unless that jockey was riding in top form. Hence he would make no long range commitments, but would wait until virtually the last minute so that he might select a boy that was riding well at the time. Obviously Ben was displeased with the way Eads was riding Whirlaway, and though Eads was the stable jockey, Ben just wouldn't take a chance with him, sentiment or no sentiment. He wanted a rider who would best suit his horse.

When Ben met me at the airport—Ruth couldn't come along because we couldn't get accommodations—he was bubbling over with enthusiasm which he immediately tried to instill in me.

"Eddie," he said, "this is the fastest horse in America right now, and with you riding him, I know he can't miss winning this Derby."

Mr. Wright was equally enthusiastic. I remembered vividly his bitter disappointment when Nellie Flag failed him in the Derby of 1935. For many years he had been looking forward to the day that his silks would be ridden to victory in this big race. He had bred Whirlaway, and he considered him the fastest horse he ever owned —if not eccentric, perhaps the best horse of all time.

Jones thought that the son of Blenheim was simply a dumb horse—that once out in the middle of the track where he couldn't see the rail his mental processes became foggy and he got lost. That's why, Jones theorized, he tore out and did all sorts of crazy things.

B.A. told me he wanted me to breeze Whirlaway a half-mile in about 50 seconds Friday morning, even though he didn't need a workout. He wanted me to accustom myself to this strange horse.

When we went out on the track, Jones told me he would be waiting at the eighth pole with his pony, and that he wanted me to skim the rail all the way and to go on the inside of the pony when we hit the furlong marker.

When I set Whirlaway down he behaved like any other horse I had ridden. He stayed in all the way for the half mile and as we approached Jones, seated on his pony at the eighth pole, he stayed right on the rail. I should add that Whirlaway was equipped with regulation blinkers.

After breezing him I lost all fear that he would run out with me. In that brief introduction I discovered that he was not a horse that could be managed—that you had to take a long hold and freeze with it. You just couldn't reach up and take a fresh hold when he wanted to turn in a run. Although I might look like a coachman I found out pretty quickly that it was the only way to handle him.

I think the English type of rider would have suited Whirlaway exceptionally well. He might have been able to hold him in check with a long rein such as they use in Britain.

Jones always plans his races well. This time he was—for him—exceptionally verbose when he gave me my riding orders. We sat down early that morning, with the Derby still ten hours or so away, and, in essence, here's what he told me.

"Eddie, I absolutely do not want you to get off with this horse. Actually it would suit me better if you were left at the post on him. If you can get away badly, that will help.

"At some part of this race you are going to be in front. If it's at the sixteenth pole, that's okay, but don't take the lead at the quarter pole, or move up to the front on this horse on the turn. Just sit back there. When you call on him, he's going to give it to you."

"The one-eyed blinker."

Jones's confidence convinced me that Whirlaway's chances to whip the Derby field were bright, indeed. The races in Florida didn't count now, nor did the failures in the Blue Grass and Derby Trial. Jones' problems were ended. He could do no more. Whirlaway was now *my* problem.

Here it is Derby Day again, only this time Churchill Downs is jammed with the greatest crowd in its history. As I said earlier, the thrill of Louisville at Derby time will never grow old hat with me. I love every bit of the pre-race festivities, and although the anxiety of the wait in the jockey room before post time for the big event is trying on one's nerves, it ends soon enough. The stewards always call the jockeys for a word or two, cautioning them against roughness in this race. That comes as a welcome interlude to break the tension.

There are eleven Derby riders in the jock's room this day, and of that number Carol Bierman and I are the only ones who ever rode a Derby winner. Buddy Haas is to ride Porter's Cap, and he's one of the stoutly backed horses. Conn McCreary is Our Boots' rider. I had beaten Whirlaway on Our Boots in the Futurity at Belmont the previous fall. But Whirlaway had turned the tables in the Breeder's Futurity at Lexington in the waning days of the season. Anyway, Our Boots is jinxed. No Belmont Futurity winner has ever won a Kentucky Derby. None had up to this time, anyhow.

Things crop up in your mind and you try to push them out. The business of the day is how you are going to get away from the starting gate. How you are going to keep a powerfully built one-thousand-two-hundred pounds of horseflesh on a straight path down that track out there? How are you going to justify the confidence that Ben Jones and Mr. Wright have reposed in you by bringing you from New York to ride the horse that is admittedly the classiest of this field, but ornery, contrary, and plain cantankerous?

Down those same creaking wooden stairs again to the saddling enclosure, where Jones and Mr. Wright and their party await you. The several bands are striking up the familiar tunes. There is hubbub and confusion here. But man! it's wonderful!

Whirlaway is really beautiful as you size him up in his stall. His coat is flaming gold and his tail, reaching nearly to the ground, a lighter, blondish hue. A thoroughbred, this fellow, even to his looks. A fine head but, verily, dumb.

And then I see it. *Jones has put a one-eyed blinker on this horse.* "What the hell is this guy thinking about," I say to myself, "running a horse for the *first time* in a one-eyed blinker in this, the biggest race in his career!"

I just couldn't believe it. I had breezed him only the day before in regular blinkers. Now, right at the last minute, B.A. has equipped him with a blinker that shades only the right eye. The left cup had been torn off.

Jones didn't try to explain to me, but I knew what he had in mind. Whirlaway could see that inside rail now, and the rest would be up to me. . . . That Jones, always thinking up new ideas!

Out on the post parade and again "My Old Kentucky Home" sends a tingle up and down your spine. A lump forms in your throat as the strains die down and you take your horse out of line for a canter. You know from the way he has pranced on the parade and the way he's behaving now that he's feeling fit and he has what it takes—the machinery. He'll do, you say.

Now we're in the gate. No. 4 is my stall compartment. The boys are chanting their litany: "No chance yet, sir; no chance; no chance, sir." Reuben White in the starter's box is closely watching this field of eleven thoroughbreds. He realizes his responsibility. He must give all of them a fair break. Eyes are on him, too.

There's not much delay. A minute and a half, that's all, but it seems very long. Then he roars, does Big Reuben, "C'mon!"

The 1941 Kentucky Derby is under way.

Dispose goes to the front. Porter's Cap, Blue Pair, Robert Morris, Our Boots, Market Wise and Staretor are next in order. Before a furlong has been run, I find myself blocked. I ease up and then move to the inside going to the first turn. Around the lower turn and into the backstretch, I just wait. At the half mile I start up after the leaders, threading my way between horses, and on the home turn Whirlaway responds to take command and then draw away, never drifting out for a moment, to win by eight lengths in 2:01 2/5, a new track record. I had never seen such power exhibited as when we hit the three-eighths pole and I called on him for his speed. He literally took off, nearly catapulting me out of the saddle. As he stretched his legs I felt as if I were flying through the air. That final rush he showed was stunning.

It was a happy Mr. Wright and a smiling Ben Jones who were waiting in the winner's circle as we cantered back to the scales. And, I should add, Mr. Arcaro was mighty happy, too.

Eddie Arcaro and Citation

Eddie Arcaro

When Citation was at his peak—after he had won the Triple Crown with consummate ease—the argument became intense among horsemen as to just how well he rated with great horses of the past. Not all who had an opinion were completely qualified to judge, though that did not deter them. In fact, the least qualified were often the most vociferous. But even among seasoned horsemen the estimate ran from "the greatest since Man o' War" to "greater than Man o' War."

Arcaro was Citation's rider and probably knew him better than anyone else, so what he has to say of this truly great horse is of particular interest. (—From I Ride to Win*)*

Man and boy, I have been on fast horses beyond number. But this Citation was a horse apart from anything else I had ever ridden. His stride was frictionless; his vast speed alarming. You could call on him at any time and, as Ben Jones said of him, he could run down any horse that ever breathed.

Citation was a particularly handsome horse, although not at all flashy. He possessed a wonderful head and was probably a little above average stature. In addition to everything else, he was intelligent. He knew his business when he got out there on the track. He seemed to have a way of knowing what was demanded of him, and he gave without stint. Riding him was like being on a machine equipped with a throttle. You opened it up and away he went. That was Citation.

After winning the Derby Trial in a proverbial romp, Citation looked to me to be the surest Derby winner of my generation. If he did win, he would be the first horse in the seventy-four runnings of that special to snare both Belmont Futurity and the Derby. But in spite of his brilliant record and the fact that the world knew he was at the very peak of his form, there were some die-hards who still insisted Coaltown was the better horse.

The Kentuckians who had seen Coaltown win at Keenland just wouldn't believe that he could be beaten in the Derby by Citation or any other man's horse. Never had they seen such a display of speed, and they could not imagine how any horse was ever going to run him down, once he had taken off. In fact there were many horse-for-horse bets made, some of them, I have been told, ranging into tall figures.

The track was sloppy on this Derby Day of 1948, and Calumet's entry was a surprising 2 to 5 in the wagering instead of the predicted 1 to 10. As I sat there in the starting gate on the horse that almost everyone expected me to guide home to victory, I was obsessed with but one question; when should I set sail for Coaltown? Everybody conceded that he would have the early foot and would be out there carving the early pace. With only six horses in

"Riding Citation was like being on a machine equipped with a throttle. You opened it up and away he went."

the race, I should not get into any trouble at the start. My job was to open up that throttle at exactly the right point in the race.

As if the battle plan had already been rehearsed, before we had gone an eighth of a mile Coaltown was six or eight lengths on top and just rolling. I stayed in second position down the back stretch. Coaltown was still eating up the ground, maybe four lengths in front as we approached the far turn. Then I asked Citation for it. As if gifted with steel springs for legs, he bounded after his stablemate. At the three-sixteenths pole we drew even. Just clucking to him I could feel him continue to surge ahead with that blazing speed, and at the end he was going away by three and a half lengths. Coaltown was second and My Request was third.

Let me tell you I was plenty scared back there while Coaltown was virtually skimming over the ground away out in front. I was following my riding orders implicitly, but I could tell that Pierson was not easing up on Coaltown one bit. He was running so easily, gobbling up the ground with each stride, that at one juncture he must have been a good dozen lengths on top.

I kept remembering what Old B.A. had told me—that the horse that Citation could not run down had not yet been born. But what is this now, I said to myself. Suppose Citation doesn't pick up Coaltown when I call on him?

Even around the Calumet barn, Coaltown had more than his share of supporters who were willing to wager that he, and not Citation, would be the Derby winner. They tell me that many of them also made horse-for-horse bets.

These stories, some of them emanating from the barn itself, began to create some doubt in my mind, too. I knew Citation, I had ridden him—but this other speed marvel I didn't know much about. I decided I would take the matter directly to Old B.A.

Seated in the Churchill Downs grandstand, I put the question quite bluntly to Ben. "B.A." I asked, "which do you think is the better horse?"

Without blinking an eye, he said: "Eddie, if I thought Coaltown would win the Derby, you'd be on him."

Whatever doubts I had were dispelled. I had so much respect for

Old Ben's judgment that I was ready then and there to wrap up this Derby.

Still I would have to be alert in the race, because the planned strategy was to have Coaltown open up as far as he could on the field. He was not to be taken back, and my orders were to stay with the pack, or a little ahead of them. What if that horse with all his speed opened up an eighth of a mile and I couldn't catch him at the finish? I'd look very foolish.

Although Jimmy, the son, was doing the actual training, it was decided, as a nice gesture, to have Ben's name go down on the program as the trainer for the Derby, so that if Calumet were to win it, Ben's name would be in the records as the trainer of four Derby winners, thus tying H. J. (Dick) Thompson, the old Bradley trainer, who had saddled that number.

I would like to emphasize one thing about this Derby. If Coaltown was ever going to beat Citation this would have had to be the day. After Citation had picked him up and stowed him away, I knew—to my own satisfaction, at least—that Coaltown had never seen the day he could beat Citation. Old Ben had called it right, again.

I doubt that any horse ever received the ovation that was extended to Citation as he was brought into the winner's circle for the presentation ceremonies and the draping around his neck of the garland of red roses. The Jones's were beaming, and Mr. Wright could hardly restrain himself as he reached out his hand to congratulate me.

There followed then a procession of successes. Under steady restraint and an easy hand ride, Citation led Vulcan's Forge to the wire in the Preakness by six lengths. That was the second jewel in the diadem of the Triple Crown. The third was added in just as easy fashion when Citation literally romped in the Belmont stakes to become the eighth in history to win all three of the spring specials, this time making the accounting by eight lengths in 2:28 1/5, equaling Count Fleet's for the mile and a half.

And so it went through the year as he continued to chew up his

"Everyone asserted that this was America's greatest race horse since Man o' War."

rivals wherever he met them and whatever the condition of the race track, and everyone asserted that this was America's greatest race horse since Man o' War. Certainly in those races Citation was the best horse I ever rode. He could beat older horses as well as those of his own age with ease. But when he was shipped to California for the Tanforan Handicap in December of 1948 and was put in an overnight race for a tune-up, I knew something was wrong. I expressed my opinion to Jimmy Jones, and he said not to let it worry me, and he would be sharper for his handicap engagement.

But he just wasn't the Citation of earlier days, even though he won the Tanforan Handicap and broke the track record that day. He was unable to extend himself and didn't seem to have the will to go on.

A few days later Citation popped an osselet and was placed in temporary retirement, which was to last over a year.

Big Red

J. A. Estes

The days are long at Belmont.
Speed they never learn.
And it's many a day since Man o' War
Has looped the upper turn.

The guineas stopped their rubbing,
The rider dropped his tack
When the word went round that Man o' War
Was coming on the track.

The crowd was hoarse with cheering
At ancient Pimlico
The day he won the Preakness—
But that was long ago.

The dust is deep at Windsor,
The good old days are done,
And many a horse is forgotten,
But they still remember one.

For he was a fiery phantom
To that multitudinous throng—
Would you wait for another one like him?
Be patient; years are long.

For here was a horse among horses,
Cast in a Titan's mold,
And the slant October sunlight
Gilded the living gold.

He was marked with the god's own giving
And winged in every part;
The look of eagles was in his eye
And Hasting's wrath in his heart.

Young Equipoise had power
To rouse the crowded stand,
And there was magic in the name
Of Greentree's Twenty Grand.

And Sarazen has sprinted,
And Gallant Fox has stayed,
And Discovery has glittered
In the wake of Cavalcade. . . .

We watch the heroes parading,
We wait, and our eyes are dim,

But we never discover another
Like him.

A foal is born at midnight
And in the frosty morn
The horseman eyes him fondly,
And a secret hope is born

But breathe it not, nor whisper,
For fear of a neighbor's scorn:
He's a chestnut colt, and he's got a star—
He may be another Man o' War.

Nay, say it aloud—be shameless.
Dream and hope and yearn,
For there's never a man among you
But waits for his return.